STUDENT UNIT GUIDE

NEW EDITION

CCEA A2 Chemistry Unit 1

Periodic Trends and Further Organic, Physical and Inorganic Chemistry

Alyn G. McFarland

PHILIP ALLAN FOR
HODDER
EDUCATION
AN HACHETTE UK COMPANY

Philip Allan, an imprint of Hodder Education, an Hachette UK company, Market Place, Deddington, Oxfordshire OX15 0SE

Orders
Bookpoint Ltd, 130 Milton Park, Abingdon, Oxfordshire OX14 4SB
tel: 01235 827827
fax: 01235 400401
e-mail: education@bookpoint.co.uk
Lines are open 9.00 a.m.–5.00 p.m., Monday to Saturday, with a 24-hour message answering service. You can also order through the Philip Allan Updates website: www.philipallan.co.uk

ISBN 978-1-4718-0015-3

First printed 2013
Impression number 5 4 3
Year 2017 2016 2015

Cover photo: Fotolia

Typeset by Integra Software Services Pvt. Ltd, Pondicherry, India

Printed in Italy

Hachette UK's policy is to use papers that are natural, renewable and recyclable products and made from wood grown in sustainable forests. The logging and manufacturing processes are expected to conform to the environmental regulations of the country of origin.

P02274

Contents

Getting the most from this book

Questions & Answers

Exam-style questions

Examiner comments on the questions
Tips on what you need to do to gain full marks, indicated by the icon ⓔ.

Sample student answers
Practise the questions, then look at the student answers that follow each set of questions.

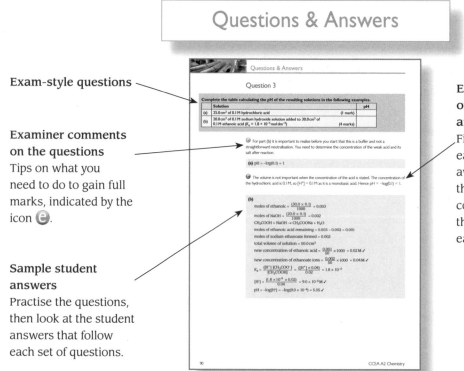

Examiner commentary on sample student answers
Find out how many marks each answer would be awarded in the exam and then read the examiner comments (preceded by the icon ⓔ) following each student answer.

About this book

This book will guide you through CCEA A2 Chemistry Unit 1: Periodic Trends and Further Organic, Physical and Inorganic Chemistry. It has two sections:

- The **Content Guidance** section covers all of A2 Unit 1 and includes helpful *examiner tips* on how to approach revision and improve exam technique. Do not skim over these tips because they provide important guidance. There are also *knowledge check* questions throughout this section, with *answers* at the end of the book. At the end of each section there is a *summary* of the key points covered.
- The **Questions and Answers** section gives sample examination questions on each topic as well as worked answers and examiner comments on the common pitfalls to avoid. The examination will consist of 10 multiple-choice questions (each with four options, A to D), followed by several structured questions. This Questions and Answers section contains many different examples of questions, but you should also refer to past papers for this unit, which are available online.

Both the Content Guidance and Questions and Answers sections are divided into the topics outlined by the CCEA specification.

General tips

- Be accurate with your learning — examiners will penalise incorrect wording.
- Follow calculations through to the end even if you think you have made a mistake. There are marks for the correct method even if the final answer is incorrect.
- Always attempt to answer a multiple-choice question even if it is a guess (you have a 25% chance of getting it right).

There is a possible total of 300 marks for AS chemistry. Both A21 and A22 are awarded out of 120 and A23 (examining practical work and planning from A21 and A22) is awarded out of 60 uniform marks, giving a possible total of 300 for A2 chemistry. This gives a total of 600 for GCE chemistry.

When answering questions involving the colour of a chemical, you must be accurate to obtain the marks. If the colour of a chemical is given in this book with a hyphen (-) between the colours then state the two colours exactly like that, including the hyphen. For example, bromine is red-brown, so both red and brown are required, separated by a hyphen.

If two or more colours are given separated by a forward slash (/), these are alternative answers and only *one* colour from this choice should be given. For example, for the yellow/orange colour of the 2,4-dinitrophenylhydrazone derivatives of aldehydes and ketones, yellow on its own or orange on its own will be accepted but *not* a combination of the two colours.

Never use a forward slash (/) when answering a colour question. If only one colour is given for a chemical then use this single colour — for example, red for the colour of the precipitate when an aldehyde is warmed with Fehling's solution. This applies to all CCEA AS and A2 examinations. Check the colour document on the CCEA chemistry microsite (www.ccea.org.uk/chemistry), then select revised GCE for further guidance should this change.

Content Guidance

From AS2, the **standard enthalpy change** of formation is the enthalpy change when 1 mol of a compound is formed from its elements under standard conditions.

The **standard lattice enthalpy** is the enthalpy change when 1 mol of an ionic compound is converted into gaseous ions.

Lattice enthalpy

Lattice enthalpy is the enthalpy change when 1 mol of an ionic compound is converted into gaseous ions. Lattice enthalpy values may be calculated using a Born–Haber cycle.

Born–Haber cycle

The Born–Haber cycle is a technique for applying Hess's law to the standard enthalpy changes that occur when an ionic compound is formed. The formation of an ionic compound, for example NaCl, can be thought of as occurring in a series of steps even though the reaction itself may not follow this route.

For sodium chloride (NaCl), the formation can be written as:

$$Na(s) + \tfrac{1}{2}Cl_2(g) \rightarrow NaCl(s)$$

The **standard enthalpy change** of formation is represented by $\Delta H_f^\ominus$.

The important energy change that we are often trying to determine is the **standard lattice enthalpy** of an ionic compound. This value is calculated using the Born–Haber cycle.

For example, for NaCl(s):

$$NaCl(s) \rightarrow Na^+(g) + Cl^-(g)$$

The standard lattice enthalpy is represented by $\Delta H_{latt}^\ominus$.

The Born–Haber cycle for NaCl can be drawn simply as shown in Figure 1.

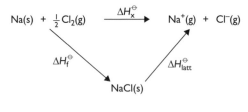

Figure 1

All enthalpy changes can be determined experimentally apart from the standard lattice enthalpy. $\Delta H_x^\ominus$ is a combination of a few standard enthalpy changes that take $Na(s) + \tfrac{1}{2}Cl_2(g)$ to $Na^+(g) + Cl^-(g)$.

The change $Na(s) + \frac{1}{2}Cl_2(g) \rightarrow Na^+(g) + Cl^-(g)$ is composed of the following steps:

1 $Na(s) \rightarrow Na(g)$

This is the atomisation of sodium. The **standard enthalpy change of atomisation** of sodium is represented by $\Delta H_a^{\ominus}$ or $\Delta H_{at}^{\ominus}$.

2 $Na(g) \rightarrow Na^+(g) + e^-$

This is the first ionisation of sodium. The **first ionisation energy** (enthalpy) is represented by $\Delta H_{IE1}^{\ominus}$.

3 $\frac{1}{2}Cl_2(g) \rightarrow Cl(g)$

This is the atomisation of chlorine. The same symbol is used for the standard enthalpy change of atomisation as for step 1 for sodium, and the definition is the same.

For diatomic elements such as chlorine, the bond dissociation enthalpy may be used.

For $Cl_2(g) \rightarrow 2Cl(g)$ the enthalpy change is the bond dissociation enthalpy or twice the standard enthalpy change of atomisation.

The **bond dissociation enthalpy** is represented by $\Delta H_{BDE}^{\ominus}$.

Examiner tip

Remember that the bond dissociation enthalpy is twice the standard enthalpy of atomisation for diatomic elements. You may need to use one times the standard enthalpy of atomisation (if 1 mol of atoms is required) or two times the standard enthalpy of atomisation (if two moles of atoms are required). If 1 mol of atoms is required you will need to use half of the bond dissociation enthalpy; if two moles of atoms are required, use one bond dissociation enthalpy.

4 $Cl(g) + e^- \rightarrow Cl^-(g)$

This is the **first electron affinity** of chlorine. It is represented by $\Delta H_{EA1}^{\ominus}$.

Examiner tip

For halides of Group II elements, two atomisations and two first electron affinities are required. For example, $Cl_2(g)$ is converted to $2Cl(g)$ and $2Cl(g)$ is converted to $2Cl^-(g)$.

A typical Born–Haber cycle diagram

Figure 2 shows a Born–Haber cycle diagram for a typical Group I halide, in this case sodium chloride (NaCl).

Examiner tip

The labels on the left and right are there to remind you what should be present at each level. Endothermic processes normally have upward arrows and exothermic processes have downward arrows. There are different forms of this type of diagram but this is the most common. You will be most often asked to complete the diagram or use it. Don't forget the electrons or the state symbols. This type of diagram can be applied to any Group I halide or hydride.

The **standard enthalpy change of atomisation** is the enthalpy change when 1 mol of gaseous atoms is formed from the element in its standard state.

Knowledge check 1

What is the definition of standard enthalpy change of atomisation?

From AS 1, the **first ionisation energy** is the energy required to convert 1 mol of gaseous atoms to 1 mol of gaseous ions with a single positive charge.

The **bond dissociation enthalpy** is the energy required to break 1 mol of a covalent bond under standard conditions.

The **first electron affinity** is the enthalpy change when 1 mol of gaseous atoms is converted to 1 mol of gaseous ions with a single negative charge.

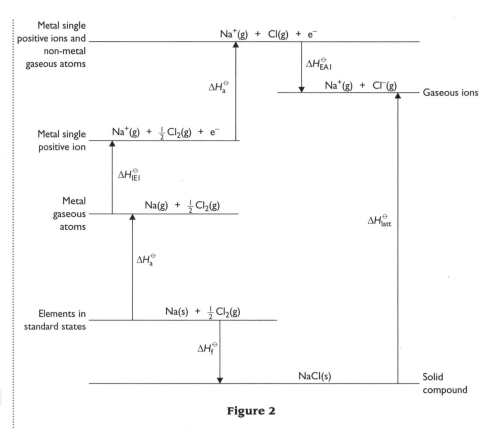

Figure 2

Worked example

The values given for a calculation might be:
- enthalpy of formation of sodium chloride ($\Delta H_f^{\ominus}$) = −411 kJ mol^{-1}
- enthalpy of atomisation of sodium ($\Delta H_a^{\ominus}$ or $\Delta H_{at}^{\ominus}$) = +108 kJ mol^{-1}
- first ionisation energy of sodium ($\Delta H_{IE1}^{\ominus}$) = +500 kJ mol^{-1}
- enthalpy of atomisation of chlorine ($\Delta H_a^{\ominus}$ or $\Delta H_{at}^{\ominus}$) = +121 kJ mol^{-1}
- first electron affinity of chlorine ($\Delta H_{EA1}^{\ominus}$) = −364 kJ mol^{-1}

$$\Delta H_{latt}^{\ominus} = -\Delta H_f^{\ominus} + \Delta H_a^{\ominus} + \Delta H_{IE1}^{\ominus} + \Delta H_a^{\ominus} + \Delta H_{EA1}^{\ominus}$$

$$\phantom{\Delta H_{latt}^{\ominus} = }NaCl \quad Na \quad Na \quad Cl \quad Cl$$

$$= +411 + 108 + 500 + 121 - 364$$

$$= +776 \text{ kJ mol}^{-1}$$

The cycle works from the beginning of the arrow for lattice enthalpy to the end of the arrow. The alternative route gives the same energy changes as predicted by Hess's law. The alternative route must take into account the direction of the arrows. If the direction is reversed then the negative of the value must be used.

This is a standard Born–Haber diagram for all Group I halides. 1 mol of the Group I metal, A, reacts with ½ mol of the halide, ½X$_2$, to form 1 mol of the solid halide, AX(s).

Born–Haber cycle for Group II halides

For Group II halides, MX_2, the Born–Haber diagram is slightly extended. The cycle in Figure 3 is for magnesium chloride ($MgCl_2$).

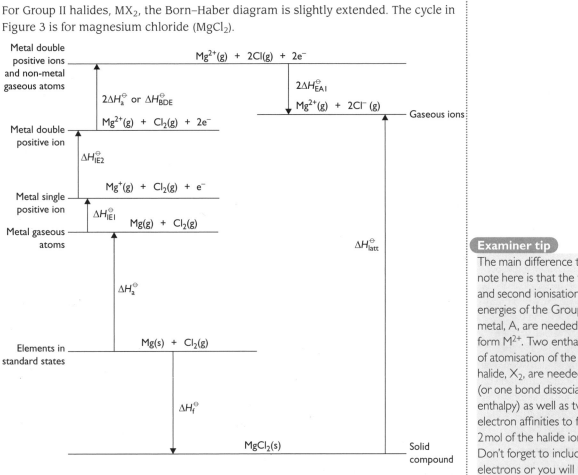

Figure 3

Examiner tip
The main difference to note here is that the first and second ionisation energies of the Group II metal, A, are needed to form M^{2+}. Two enthalpies of atomisation of the halide, X_2, are needed (or one bond dissociation enthalpy) as well as two electron affinities to form 2 mol of the halide ion, X^-. Don't forget to include the electrons or you will lose all the marks for that level.

Worked example

Lattice enthalpy can be calculated since we know the other values in the Born–Haber cycle:

- enthalpy of formation of magnesium chloride ($\Delta H_f^{\ominus}$) = $-642\,kJ\,mol^{-1}$
- enthalpy of atomisation of magnesium ($\Delta H_a^{\ominus}$) = $+150\,kJ\,mol^{-1}$
- first ionisation energy of magnesium ($\Delta H_{IE1}^{\ominus}$) = $+736\,kJ\,mol^{-1}$
- second ionisation energy of magnesium ($\Delta H_{IE2}^{\ominus}$) = $+1450\,kJ\,mol^{-1}$
- bond dissociation enthalpy of chlorine ($\Delta H_{BDE}^{\ominus}$) = $+242\,kJ\,mol^{-1}$
- first electron affinity of chlorine ($\Delta H_{EA1}^{\ominus}$) = $-364\,kJ\,mol^{-1}$

$$\Delta H_{latt}^{\ominus} = -\Delta H_f^{\ominus} + \Delta H_a^{\ominus} + \Delta H_{IE1}^{\ominus} + \Delta H_{IE2}^{\ominus} + \Delta H_{BDE}^{\ominus} + 2\Delta H_{EA1}^{\ominus}$$

 $MgCl_2$ Mg Mg Mg Cl_2 Cl

 = +642 + 150 + 736 + 1450 + 242 − 2(364)

 = $+2492\,kJ\,mol^{-1}$

The **enthalpy of hydration** is defined as the enthalpy change when I mol of gaseous ions is converted into I mol of aqueous ions.

The **enthalpy of solution** is defined as the enthalpy change when I mol of a solute dissolves in water.

Understanding enthalpy changes in a Born–Haber cycle

The enthalpy changes in a Born–Haber cycle are summarised in Table 1.

Table 1

Enthalpy	Exothermic (ΔH negative)	Endothermic (ΔH positive)
Lattice enthalpy		✓
Enthalpy of formation	mostly ✓	
Enthalpy of atomisation		✓
Bond dissociation enthalpy		✓
First ionisation energy		✓
Second ionisation energy		✓
First electron affinity	✓	

The lattice enthalpy depends on the charge on the ions and the size of the ions. Smaller ions are more closely packed in the lattice and so are more attracted to each other. Ions with a high charge are more attracted to each other as well. For example:

- The lattice enthalpy for NaCl is $+776\,\text{kJ}\,\text{mol}^{-1}$ but that for NaF is $+915\,\text{kJ}\,\text{mol}^{-1}$. The F^- ion is smaller than the Cl^- ion, so the ions in NaF can pack closer together in the lattice and so lattice enthalpy is greater as the attraction is greater.
- The lattice enthalpy for $MgCl_2$ is $+2494\,\text{kJ}\,\text{mol}^{-1}$ but that for MgO is $+3933\,\text{kJ}\,\text{mol}^{-1}$. The lattice enthalpy for $MgCl_2$ is greater than that for NaCl due to the 2+ charge on the magnesium ion. Note that the lattice enthalpy for MgO is very high (and hence it is very stable and has a very high melting point) due to the 2+ and 2− charges on the small ions.

Enthalpy of solution

Ionic compounds dissolve in water when the ionic lattice breaks up (lattice enthalpy) and the polar water molecules form bonds with the ions (**enthalpy of hydration**).

$$\text{enthalpy of solution} = \text{lattice enthalpy} + \text{enthalpy of hydration}$$

For sodium chloride:

$$\Delta H_{sol}^{\ominus} = \Delta H_{latt}^{\ominus} + \Delta H_{hyd}^{\ominus} + \Delta H_{hyd}^{\ominus}$$
$$\text{NaCl} \quad\quad \text{NaCl} \quad\quad \text{Na}^+ \quad\quad \text{Cl}^-$$

The balance of the break-up of the ionic lattice and the bonds forming with water determines the **enthalpy of solution**.

The enthalpy of solution can be determined from other enthalpy values. For example:

$$\text{NaCl(s)} + \text{(aq)} \rightarrow \text{Na}^+\text{(aq)} + \text{Cl}^-\text{(aq)} \qquad \Delta H_{sol}^{\ominus} = +5\,\text{kJ}\,\text{mol}^{-1}$$

The lattice enthalpy for sodium chloride is represented by the equation:

$$\text{NaCl(s)} \rightarrow \text{Na}^+\text{(g)} + \text{Cl}^-\text{(g)} \qquad \Delta H_{latt}^{\ominus} = +776\,\text{kJ}\,\text{mol}^{-1}$$

The enthalpy of hydration is represented by:

$$Na^+(g) + (aq) \rightarrow Na^+(aq) \qquad \Delta H_{hyd}^{\ominus} = -407 \, kJ \, mol^{-1}$$

$$Cl^-(g) + (aq) \rightarrow Cl^-(aq) \qquad \Delta H_{hyd}^{\ominus} = -364 \, kJ \, mol^{-1}$$

These enthalpy changes fit together in the cycle shown in Figure 4.

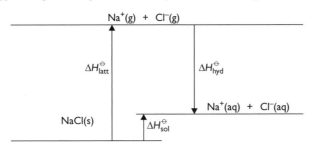

Figure 4

$$\Delta H_{sol}^{\ominus} = (+776) + (-407) + (-364) = +5 \, kJ \, mol^{-1}$$

It is clear that 5 kJ of energy are released when 1 mol of NaCl dissolves in water to form a solution. It is not suggested that when NaCl dissolves in water, the ionic lattice breaks up into scattered gaseous ions, which then dissolve. However, it allows an alternative route for calculating enthalpy of solution values. A simpler diagram for calculation of solution may be like Figure 5.

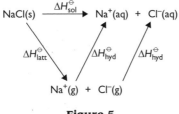

Figure 5

When ionic compounds dissolve in water the polar water molecules are attracted to the charged ions. The δ– O atoms in H_2O molecules are attracted to the positive ions and the δ+ H atoms in H_2O molecules are attracted to the negative ions (Figure 6).

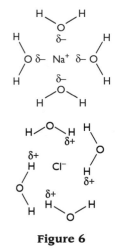

Figure 6

Summary

- Lattice enthalpy is the enthalpy of the breaking of 1 mol of an ionic compound into gaseous ions, and is endothermic (ΔH is positive).
- A Born–Haber cycle allows us to calculate the lattice enthalpy from atomisation enthalpy values, ionisation enthalpy values, bond dissociation enthalpy values, electron affinities and enthalpy of formation values.
- The bond dissociation enthalpy value for a halogen is twice the enthalpy of atomisation value.
- Enthalpy of solution is the total of the lattice enthalpy and the enthalpy of hydration of the ions.

Enthalpy, entropy and free energy

A reaction that happens of its own accord without any external help is called a spontaneous reaction. Some spontaneous reactions are endothermic:

$$KCl(s) + (aq) \rightarrow K^+(aq) + Cl^-(aq) \qquad \Delta H^\ominus = +19\,kJ\,mol^{-1}$$

$$H_2O(s) \rightarrow H_2O(l) \qquad \Delta H^\ominus = +6\,kJ\,mol^{-1}$$

$$H_2O(l) \rightarrow H_2O(g) \qquad \Delta H^\ominus = +44\,kJ\,mol^{-1}$$

$$(NH_4)_2CO_3(s) \rightarrow 2NH_3(g) + CO_2(g) + H_2O(g) \qquad \Delta H^\ominus = +68\,kJ\,mol^{-1}$$

Entropy is a measure of disorder or randomness in a system.

Table 2

Substance	Entropy ($J\,K^{-1}\,mol^{-1}$)
C (diamond)	5.7
CO(g)	197.6
CO_2(g)	213.6
Si(s)	18.8
$CaCO_3$(s)	92.9
CaO(s)	39.7
H_2O(s)	48
H_2O(l)	69.9
H_2O(g)	189
Ne(g)	146.2

The change in enthalpy cannot be the only factor that determines whether a reaction is spontaneous or not. All four of the reactions above have one thing in common — an increase in disorder. All of them show a change from an ordered structure to a random structure. The degree of disorder or randomness in a system is measured and is called **entropy**.

A crystalline solid with a highly ordered arrangement has low entropy. When it melts, the system becomes less ordered (it is impossible to tell exactly where each ion/particle is relative to each other), so the entropy has increased.

Entropy is given the symbol S and standard entropy $S^\ominus$. Change in entropy is represented by $\Delta S^\ominus$. An increase in the disorder of a system has a positive $\Delta S^\ominus$ value. Entropy is measured in $J\,K^{-1}\,mol^{-1}$. Some entropy ($S^\ominus$) values are given in Table 2.

Worked examples

$$NH_4NO_3(s) \rightarrow N_2O(g) + 2H_2O(g)$$

1 mol of solid ammonium nitrate forms 1 mol of dinitrogen oxide gas and 2 mol of water vapour. This will have a positive $\Delta S^\ominus$ value as the gases are much less ordered than the crystalline solid (ammonium nitrate). Under standard conditions the water formed in the equation above would be a liquid, which is more ordered than a gas, so the $\Delta S^\ominus$ would be less positive.

$$CaO(s) + H_2O(l) \rightarrow Ca(OH)_2(s) \qquad \Delta S^\ominus \text{ is negative}$$

1 mol of solid + 1 mol of liquid (less ordered) forms 1 mol of solid (ordered).

$$CaCO_3(s) \rightarrow CaO(s) + CO_2(g) \qquad \Delta S^\ominus \text{ is positive}$$

1 mol of solid forms 1 mol of solid and 1 mol of gas (less ordered).

Calculating $\Delta S^\ominus$ values

If you are given standard entropy values for the reactants and the products then the value of $\Delta S^\ominus$ can be calculated.

Examiner tip

Only $\Delta S^\ominus$ values need to have a positive or negative sign. $S^\ominus$ values are always positive. Solids are more ordered than liquids/solutions, which are more ordered than gases. From the equation of a reaction, it is often possible to tell if $\Delta S^\ominus$ is positive or negative. A reaction is often called a system, so often we say that the entropy of the system has decreased or increased, meaning that $\Delta S^\ominus$ is negative or positive respectively.

Knowledge check 2

What does $\Delta S^\ominus$ mean?

Worked example 1

Given the following standard entropy values:

chlorine	Cl_2	$= 223\,J\,K^{-1}\,mol^{-1}$
ethene	$CH_2{=}CH_2$	$= 219\,J\,K^{-1}\,mol^{-1}$
1,2–dichlororethane	CH_2ClCH_2Cl	$= 208\,J\,K^{-1}\,mol^{-1}$

calculate $\Delta S^\ominus$ for the reaction:

$$CH_2{=}CH_2(g) + Cl_2(g) \rightarrow CH_2ClCH_2Cl(l)$$

$\Delta S^\ominus$ = sum of $S^\ominus$ for the products – sum of $S^\ominus$ for the reactants

$\Delta S^\ominus$ = (208) – (223 + 219) = 208 – 442 = $-234\,J\,K^{-1}\,mol^{-1}$

The negative value of $\Delta S^\ominus$ indicates an increase in order, which is what we would expect when 2 mol of gas form 1 mol of liquid.

Examiner tip
For all $\Delta S^\ominus$ calculations the 'per mole' in the equation must be taken into account. If 2 mol of a reactant are used then 2 mol of the entropy value for this substance are used.

Worked example 2

$$N_2(g) + 3H_2(g) \rightarrow 2NH_3(g)$$

$S^\ominus$ values:

$N_2(g) = 191.6\,J\,K^{-1}\,mol^{-1}$

$H_2(g) = 130.6\,J\,K^{-1}\,mol^{-1}$

$NH_3(g) = 192.3\,J\,K^{-1}\,mol^{-1}$

Calculate the value of $\Delta S^\ominus$ for this reaction.

$\Delta S^\ominus$ = sum of $S^\ominus$ for the products – sum of $S^\ominus$ for the reactants

$\Delta S^\ominus$ = 2(192.3) – (191.6) – 3(130.6) = $-198.8\,J\,K^{-1}\,mol^{-1}$

This reaction shows a decrease in entropy as the system becomes more ordered, i.e. 4 mol of gas become 2 mol of gas.

Feasibility of a reaction

In all feasible and spontaneous reactions $\Delta G^\ominus$ must be less than zero.

$$\Delta G^\ominus = \Delta H^\ominus - T\Delta S^\ominus$$

The term on the left hand side ($\Delta G^\ominus$) is called Gibbs free energy. T is the temperature measured in kelvin (K). In order for a reaction to be feasible, $\Delta G^\ominus$ must be negative.

For a reaction to be feasible/spontaneous $\Delta G^\ominus$ must be negative.

Worked example 1

(a) Show that the thermal decomposition of sodium carbonate is not feasible at 1200 K.

$$Na_2CO_3(s) \rightarrow Na_2O(s) + CO_2(g) \quad \Delta H^\ominus = +323\,kJ\,mol^{-1}$$
$$\Delta S^\ominus = +153.7\,J\,K^{-1}\,mol^{-1}$$

Examiner tip
You can calculate if a reaction is feasible at a certain temperature by calculating $\Delta G^\ominus$. You can calculate the temperature at which a reaction becomes feasible using $\Delta G^\ominus$ and $\Delta H^\ominus$, assuming that $\Delta G^\ominus$ is < 0 for a feasible reaction.

Knowledge check 3
What are the units of $\Delta G^\ominus$?

$\Delta G^{\ominus}$ has units of $kJ\,mol^{-1}$, exactly like $\Delta H^{\ominus}$, so the units of $\Delta S^{\ominus}$ must be changed to $kJ\,K^{-1}\,mol^{-1}$. This is achieved by dividing $\Delta S^{\ominus}$ by 1000.
So $\Delta S^{\ominus}$ is $+0.1537\,kJ\,K^{-1}\,mol^{-1}$.

$$\Delta G^{\ominus} = \Delta H^{\ominus} - T\Delta S^{\ominus}$$

$$\Delta G^{\ominus} = 323 - (1200 \times 0.1537) = +139\,kJ\,mol^{-1}$$

Because $\Delta G^{\ominus}$ is positive the reaction is not feasible at this temperature.

(b) At what temperature does it become feasible?

To find the temperature at which the reaction becomes feasible, we need to work out the temperature at which $\Delta G^{\ominus}$ becomes less than 0.

$$\Delta G^{\ominus} < 0 \text{ so} \qquad \Delta H^{\ominus} - T\Delta S^{\ominus} < 0$$

$$323 - T(0.1537) < 0$$

$$323 < 0.1537T$$

$$2101.5 < T$$

So T must be greater than 2101.5 K for the reaction to be feasible.

Examiner tip
To determine the temperature where a reaction changes from not feasible to feasible, divide $\Delta H^{\ominus}$ by $\Delta S^{\ominus}$, but remember to make sure $\Delta S^{\ominus}$ is in $kJ\,K^{-1}\,mol^{-1}$. Remember that where $\Delta G^{\ominus} = 0$, the reaction is not feasible; $\Delta G^{\ominus}$ must be *less than* zero.

Examiner tip
2101.5 K is the same as 1828.5°C. To convert between the Kelvin and Celsius temperature scale, simply subtract 273. To convert between Celsius and Kelvin, add 273.

Examiner tip
You should also revise Hess's law calculations from the Energetics section of AS2 because these often form part of an entropy question at A2.

Factors affecting feasibility of a reaction

The feasibility of a reaction depends on whether a reaction is endothermic or exothermic and also whether there is an increase in entropy or a decrease in entropy. Table 3 shows how these factors affect ΔG and the feasibility of a reaction.

Table 3

$\Delta H^{\ominus}$	$\Delta S^{\ominus}$	$\Delta G^{\ominus} = \Delta H^{\ominus} - T\Delta S^{\ominus}$	Feasibility
Negative	Negative	May be positive or negative	Feasible below certain temperatures
Negative	Positive	Always negative	Feasible at any temperature
Positive	Negative	Always positive	Not feasible at any temperature
Positive	Positive	May be positive or negative	Feasible above certain temperatures

Summary

- Standard entropy ($S^{\ominus}$) is measured in $J\,K^{-1}\,mol^{-1}$. Entropy is a measure of disorder.
- $\Delta S^{\ominus}$ = sum of the standard entropy values of the products − sum of the standard entropy values of the reactants.
- $\Delta G^{\ominus}$ is Gibbs free energy and is measured in $kJ\,mol^{-1}$.
- $\Delta G^{\ominus} = \Delta H^{\ominus} - T\Delta S^{\ominus}$, where T is the temperature in kelvin, $\Delta S^{\ominus}$ is the standard entropy change and $\Delta H^{\ominus}$ is the enthalpy change of the reaction.
- $\Delta S^{\ominus}$ is measured in $J\,K^{-1}\,mol^{-1}$ and it must be divided by 1000 to convert to $kJ\,K^{-1}\,mol^{-1}$ to calculate $\Delta G^{\ominus}$.
- For a reaction to be feasible, $\Delta G^{\ominus} < 0$.

Kinetics

Conventions

Kinetics is the study of the rate of a chemical reaction. The rate of a reaction can be measured according to how fast the concentration of a reactant is decreasing or how fast the concentration of a product is increasing. The units of rate are concentration per unit time — for example, $mol\,dm^{-3}\,s^{-1}$ (mol per dm^3 per second).

Rate equation

The rate equation is an expression showing how the rate of reaction is linked to the concentration of the reactants. Rate is equal to the rate constant (k) multiplied by the concentration of each reactant raised to certain whole number powers (called orders).

The rate equation for the general reaction $A + B \rightarrow C + D$ is:

$$rate = k[A]^x[B]^y$$

where x is the order of reaction with respect to reactant A, y is the order of reaction with respect to reactant B and k is the rate constant.

The overall order of the reaction is the sum of all the orders in the rate equation. In this general example it would be $x + y$.

Units of the rate constant

Rate has units of $mol\,dm^{-3}\,s^{-1}$ and concentration has units of $mol\,dm^{-3}$. The units of the rate constant, k, depend on the overall order of reaction, and can be calculated as follows.

For a general rate equation, $rate = k[A]^2[B]^1$, the overall order is 3 (2 + 1).

$$rate = k \times (concentration)^3$$

Putting in the units:

$$mol\,dm^{-3}\,s^{-1} = k(mol\,dm^{-3})^3$$

Rearranging to find k:

$$k = \frac{mol\,dm^{-3}\,s^{-1}}{(mol\,dm^{-3})^3} = \frac{mol\,dm^{-3}\,s^{-1}}{mol^3\,dm^{-9}}$$

Treat each term separately:

$$\frac{mol}{mol^3} = mol^{-2} \text{ and } \frac{dm^{-3}}{dm^{-9}} = dm^{-3-(-9)} = dm^6$$

units of the rate constant $k = \mathbf{mol^{-2}\,dm^6\,s^{-1}}$

Table 4 shows the units of the rate constant for some overall orders.

Table 4

Overall order of reaction	Units of rate constant, k
1	s^{-1}
2	$mol^{-1}\,dm^3\,s^{-1}$
3	$mol^{-2}\,dm^6\,s^{-1}$
4	$mol^{-3}\,dm^9\,s^{-1}$
5	$mol^{-4}\,dm^{12}\,s^{-1}$

Determining orders of reaction and the rate constant and its units

Often questions are set with experimental data and you are asked to determine the rate of reaction with respect to one or several reactants, or write a rate equation and calculate the value and units of the rate constant.

Worked example 1

For the general reaction $A + B + C \rightarrow D + E$ the rate equation is:

$$\text{rate} = [A]^0[B]^2[C]$$

- The order is zero with respect to A, second with respect to B and first with respect to C.
- If you treble the concentration of A, this will not change the rate as $(\times 3)^0 = (\times 1)$
- If you treble the concentration of B, this will multiply the rate by a factor of nine as $(\times 3)^2 = (\times 9)$.
- If you treble the concentration of C, this will triple the rate as $(\times 3)^1 = (\times 3)$.
- If you treble all the reactants, A, B and C, this will multiply the rate by a factor of 27 as $(\times 3)^0(\times 3)^2(\times 3)^1 = (\times 1)(\times 9)(\times 3) = (\times 27)$.

Worked example 2

In the reaction $A + B \rightarrow C + D$, doubling the concentration of A doubles the rate of reaction, whereas when the concentration of B is doubled, this has no effect on the rate.

- Doubling [A] doubles the rate, so order with respect to A is first.
- Doubling [B] has no effect on the rate, so the order with respect to B is zero.
- Rate equation is:

$$\text{rate} = k[A]$$

You can write rate = $k[A][B]^0$ but zero-order reactants are usually left out.

Worked example 3

The oxidation of nitrogen monoxide is represented by the equation:

$$2NO(g) + O_2(g) \rightarrow 2NO_2(g)$$

The kinetics of this reaction were studied and the following results recorded:

Experiment	Initial concentration of NO × 10^{-3}/mol dm^{-3}	Initial concentration of O$_2$ × 10^{-3}/mol dm^{-3}	Initial rate × 10^{-5}/mol dm^{-3} s^{-1}
1	4	1	6
2	8	1	24
3	12	1	54
4	8	2	48
5	12	3	162

Using these results, deduce the order of the reaction with respect to nitrogen monoxide and oxygen, write an overall rate equation and then deduce the value and units of the rate constant.

Experiment 1 to experiment 2

[NO] ×2   [O_2] stays the same   Rate ×4

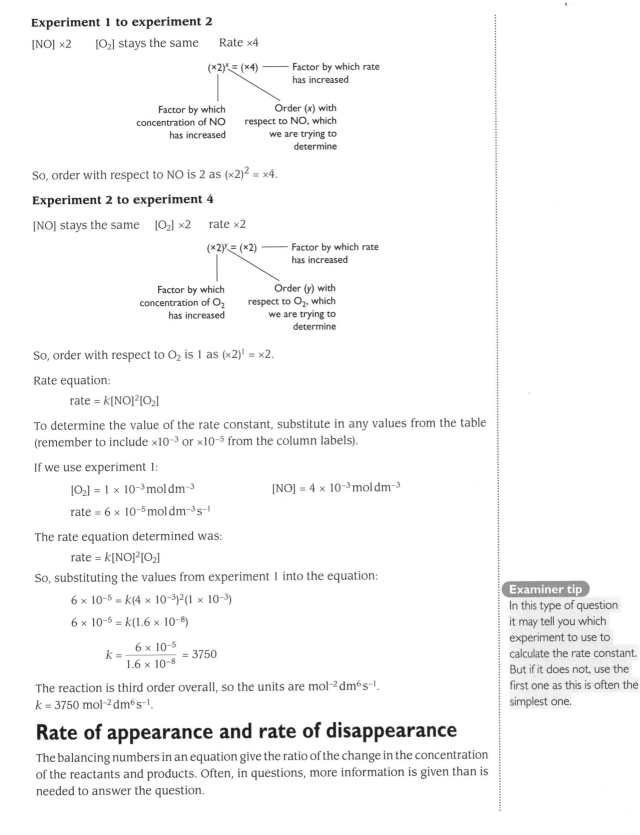

$(\times 2)^x = (\times 4)$ ——— Factor by which rate has increased

Factor by which concentration of NO has increased

Order (x) with respect to NO, which we are trying to determine

So, order with respect to NO is 2 as $(\times 2)^2 = \times 4$.

Experiment 2 to experiment 4

[NO] stays the same   [O_2] ×2   rate ×2

$(\times 2)^y = (\times 2)$ ——— Factor by which rate has increased

Factor by which concentration of O_2 has increased

Order (y) with respect to O_2, which we are trying to determine

So, order with respect to O_2 is 1 as $(\times 2)^1 = \times 2$.

Rate equation:

$$\text{rate} = k[NO]^2[O_2]$$

To determine the value of the rate constant, substitute in any values from the table (remember to include $\times 10^{-3}$ or $\times 10^{-5}$ from the column labels).

If we use experiment 1:

$[O_2] = 1 \times 10^{-3}\,\text{mol}\,\text{dm}^{-3}$ $[NO] = 4 \times 10^{-3}\,\text{mol}\,\text{dm}^{-3}$

$\text{rate} = 6 \times 10^{-5}\,\text{mol}\,\text{dm}^{-3}\,\text{s}^{-1}$

The rate equation determined was:

$$\text{rate} = k[NO]^2[O_2]$$

So, substituting the values from experiment 1 into the equation:

$$6 \times 10^{-5} = k(4 \times 10^{-3})^2(1 \times 10^{-3})$$

$$6 \times 10^{-5} = k(1.6 \times 10^{-8})$$

$$k = \frac{6 \times 10^{-5}}{1.6 \times 10^{-8}} = 3750$$

The reaction is third order overall, so the units are $\text{mol}^{-2}\,\text{dm}^6\,\text{s}^{-1}$.
$k = 3750\,\text{mol}^{-2}\,\text{dm}^6\,\text{s}^{-1}$.

Rate of appearance and rate of disappearance

The balancing numbers in an equation give the ratio of the change in the concentration of the reactants and products. Often, in questions, more information is given than is needed to answer the question.

Examiner tip

In this type of question it may tell you which experiment to use to calculate the rate constant. But if it does not, use the first one as this is often the simplest one.

Worked example

The equation below represents the oxidation of bromide ions using an acidified solution of bromate(v) ions, BrO_3^-.

$$BrO_3^-(aq) + 6H^+(aq) + 5Br^-(aq) \rightarrow 3Br_2(aq) + 3H_2O(l)$$

The rate equation for this reaction is:

$$rate = k[BrO_3^-][Br^-][H^+]$$

If the rate of disappearance of bromate(v) ions, BrO_3^-, is $2.0 \times 10^{-3}\,mol\,dm^{-3}\,s^{-1}$, what is the rate of appearance of bromine?

If 1 mol of bromate(v) ions were to disappear, 3 mol of bromine would appear, based on the ratio (1:3) in the ionic equation.

If $2.0 \times 10^{-3}\,mol\,dm^{-3}$ of bromate(v) ions are disappearing every second, then $6.0 \times 10^{-3}\,mol\,dm^{-3}$ of bromine are appearing every second.

Factors affecting rate

Rate is directly dependent on concentration of reactants, as shown in the rate equation:

$$rate \propto concentration \text{ (rate is proportional to concentration)}$$

Explaining factors affecting rate

Reaction rate depends on the number of successful collisions between reacting particles in a given period of time. The number of collisions can be affected by changes in **temperature**, **pressure** and **concentration** and the **presence of a catalyst**. A successful collision is one in which the reacting particles have enough energy to react (i.e. possess at least the activation energy).

Temperature

Increasing the temperature increases the energy of the reacting particles, which leads to an increase in the number of collisions. This causes an increase in the number of successful collisions in a given period of time, which increases the rate of reaction.

Pressure

Increasing the pressure pushes the reacting particles closer together, which increases the number of collisions. This causes an increase in the number of successful collisions in a given period of time, which increases the rate of reaction.

Concentration

Increasing the concentration of the reactant(s) increases the number of reacting particles, which leads to an increased number of collisions. This causes an increase in the number of successful collisions in a given period of time, which increases the rate of reaction.

Examiner tip

This is a much easier question than would first appear. The rate equation is not needed to answer this question. Often this type of question is given as a multiple-choice question and the extra information of the rate equation is there to confuse you. Be careful!

Examiner tip

Rate is also dependent on temperature and activation energy but these factors are not seen in the rate equation. The activation energy is affected by the presence of a **catalyst**. As temperature increases, the rate constant, k, also increases. When a catalyst is present, activation energy is lowered but the rate constant is increased.

A **catalyst** is defined as a substance that increases the rate of reaction by providing an alternative reaction pathway with lower activation energy.

Presence of a catalyst

A catalyst provides an alternative reaction pathway of lower activation energy, which increases the number of successful collisions and so increases the rate of reaction. A reaction with high activation energy will have a low rate constant.

Maxwell–Boltzmann distribution

The Maxwell–Boltzmann distribution in Figure 7 shows how a reaction with high activation energy has few molecules with enough energy to react. The value of the rate constant for such a reaction would be low, giving a low rate of reaction.

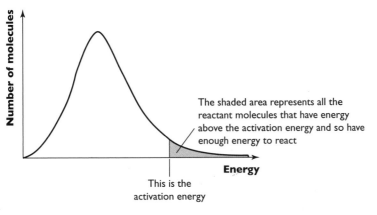

Figure 7

Examiner tip
The factor affecting rate can be explained using a distribution of molecular energies plot (Maxwell–Boltzmann distribution). Revise this topic from AS2 Kinetics — how a Maxwell–Boltzmann distribution changes with changes in temperature and the presence of a catalyst.

Methods of determining rate of reaction

The rate of a chemical reaction may be an **initial rate** of reaction or it may be **progressive rates** taken during the reaction.

- The initial rate is often referred to as the rate at time zero seconds (or $t = 0\,s$) when the reaction has just started. At this point the rate is dependent on the concentrations of the reactants added at $t = 0\,s$.
- Progressive rates are measurements taken as the reaction proceeds. The rate of reaction decreases as the reaction proceeds and the reactants are used up. Methods of measuring initial rate values relate these to the concentration of the reactant at $t = 0\,s$. Progressive rate methods can measure the rate at certain points during the reaction and relate this directly to the concentration of reactants at these times. This may seem more complex but it simply relies on being able to measure the concentration of a reactant directly during the reaction.

Rate measurements

Rate measurements are based on a measurable concentration of a reactant or product. The methods depend on the reactant or product chosen. All are measured against time as their change in concentration against time gives a measure of rate of reaction. The following methods can be used to measure the concentration of a substance against time.

- If the substance is coloured, a colorimeter can be used to measure its concentration. Often a calibration curve is used. This is a previously drawn curve relating absorbance values from the colorimeter to known concentrations of solutions of the coloured substance. It shows a directly proportional relationship. Any absorbance values can be directly converted to a concentration value using the calibration curve.

- If a gas is released, a gas syringe can be used to measure gas volume (which is the same as gas concentration), or the change in mass can be recorded.

- If a substance can be titrated, a sample of the reaction mixture can be taken and quenched and titrated to determine concentration. Quenching can be chemical (adding a chemical that removes another reactant) or by cooling the reaction rapidly to stop the reaction at the time when the sample was taken.

- If H^+ or OH^- ions are a reactant or a product, the change in pH can be measured using a pH meter (this can also be titrated with a standard solution of alkali for H^+ ions or a standard solution of acid for OH^-).

Initial rate methods

Choose a **product** whose concentration is measurable (this could be gas volume of the product, colour, pH value or directly determined by titration).

For one reactant, set up a series of experiments using a range of concentrations.

Plot graphs of measurable quantity against time. This could be gas volume against time, absorbance against time, pH against time or concentration against time determined by titration. Determine the initial gradient to determine initial rate at $t = 0\,s$ by drawing a tangent at $t = 0\,s$ and determine its gradient. This is the initial rate of reaction.

Determining initial rate of a reaction from a graph of gas volume against time

A **gas syringe** is a ground glass syringe that is attached to a sealed reaction vessel and measures the volume of gas produced. This is measured against time and a graph of gas volume against time is plotted (Figure 8). The initial gradient gives a measure of the initial rate of reaction.

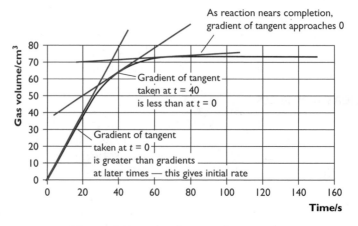

Figure 8 Example of a gas volume graph

Example of a graph showing change in mass against time

Reactions in which a gas is produced can also be monitored by measuring the mass over a period of time. The graph (Figure 9) decreases and again an initial tangent gives a measure of rate of reaction.

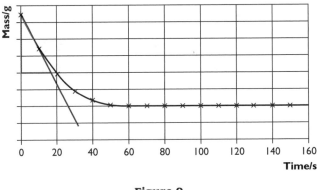

Figure 9

Graphs of rate against concentration

Repeat the experiment for the other concentrations of this reactant. This will give you initial rate values for different concentrations of the reactant you have chosen when you take tangents at $t = 0$ s. Then plot a graph of initial rate against concentration of this reactant. The shape of the graph of rate against concentration gives the order with respect to this reactant.

Figure 10 shows the graphs expected for orders 0, 1 and 2 for the reactant investigated.

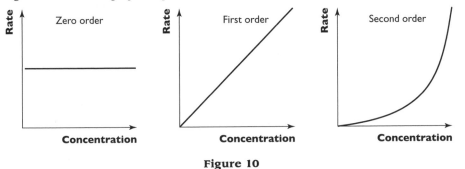

Figure 10

Progressive rate method

For this method, work out if the concentration of a reactant can be determined directly. For example:

- Hydrogen ion concentration $[H^+]$ is determined directly from pH measurements. Make sure no other ions would interfere, such as OH^- ions or a different acidic or alkaline product.
- Concentration of the coloured reactant is determined from absorbance using a calibration curve.
- A specific reactant can be titrated.

Allow the reaction to progress and take readings (absorbance/pH) or take samples at various times (samples should be quenched to stop reaction and titrated — quenching can be carried out by rapid cooling/adding large quantities of cold water/chemical quenching). Plot a graph of concentration against time for this reactant. The shape of graph gives the order with respect to this reactant.

Graphs of concentration against time

Figure 11 shows the graphs expected for orders 0, 1 and 2 for the reactant investigated.

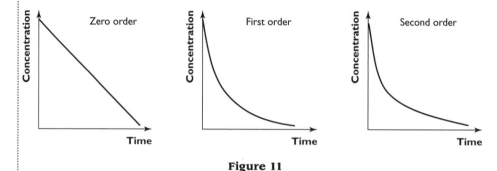

Figure 11

The gradient at various points may be taken to determine the rate of reaction. The slope of these graphs gives the rate (change in concentration against time).

An example of using a graph of concentration against time

For a coloured reactant we can use progressive rate methods. This means one experiment is carried out and the absorbance values are converted to concentration using the calibration curve. A graph of concentration against time is drawn and often the shape of this curve can give the order with respect to the coloured reactant. A gradient of a tangent at any concentration on the graph is a measure of rate at that concentration (Figure 12). The rate can then be related to the concentration and the order determined as shown before, or a graph of rate against concentration can be drawn. The shape of this graph gives the order of reaction with respect to the reactant the concentration of which you were changing.

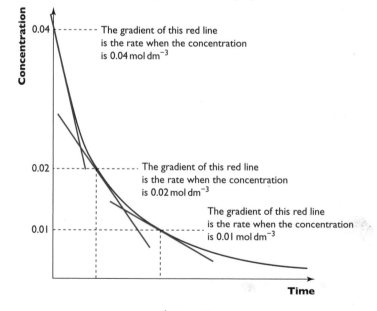

Figure 12

CCEA A2 Chemistry

Graphs of rate against concentration may be plotted for a clearer order. The values determined from the gradient at different concentrations are used. The graphs of rate against concentration are as shown in the section on initial rate methods, and these allow determination of order.

Mechanism related to order of reaction

Halogenoalkanes are hydrolysed by hydroxide ions, OH⁻. The mechanism is nucleophilic substitution but its molecularity depends on the nature of the halogenoalkane. The molecularity is the number of species involved in the **rate-determining step**.

Hydrolysis of primary halogenoalkanes

Primary (1°) halogenoalkanes undergo S_N2 hydrolysis.

The general rate equation would be:

rate = k[1° halogenoalkane][OH⁻]

The reaction profile for this hydrolysis has a transition state as shown in Figure 13. The transition state is the negatively charged complex where both the OH and halogen atom are attached by weak bonds.

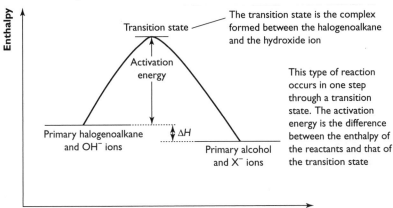

The transition state is the complex formed between the halogenoalkane and the hydroxide ion

This type of reaction occurs in one step through a transition state. The activation energy is the difference between the enthalpy of the reactants and that of the transition state

Figure 13

Hydrolysis of tertiary halogenoalkanes

Tertiary (3°) halogenoalkanes undergo S_N1 hydrolysis.

The general rate equation would be:

rate = k[3° halogenoalkane]

The reaction profile for this hydrolysis has two transition states and a reactive intermediate (Figure 14). The reactive intermediate is the positively charged carbocation in this mechanism.

> **Examiner tip**
> Data on the kinetics of hydrolysis of halogenoalkanes may be given and you may be asked to determine which is primary or tertiary, based on the calculated orders. Remember that the order with respect to OH⁻ ions will be zero for tertiary halogenoalkanes.

> **Examiner tip**
> You should revise the mechanisms for the hydrolysis of primary and tertiary halogenoalkanes from AS 2 Halogenoalkanes, and be able to draw these mechanisms.

> **Examiner tip**
> The overall order of hydrolysis of primary halogenoalkanes is 2. The reaction is first order with respect to the halogenoalkane and first order with respect to OH⁻ ions. Two species are involved in the rate-determining step, so the molecularity is 2.

> The **rate-determining step** is the slowest step in a mechanism for a reaction.

> **Examiner tip**
> The overall order of hydrolysis of tertiary halogenoalkanes is 1. The reaction is first order with respect to the halogenoalkane and zero order with respect to OH⁻ ions. One species is involved in the rate-determining step, so the molecularity is 1.

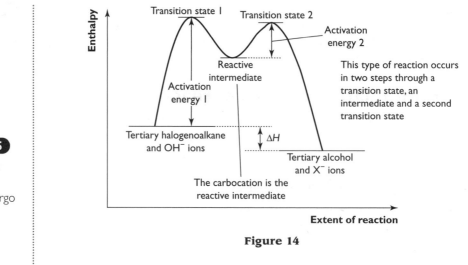

Figure 14

Name the mechanism by which tertiary halogenoalkanes undergo hydrolysis.

Summary

- The rate law states that the rate is proportional to the concentration of the reactants raised to the power of the orders of reaction with respect to each reactant.
- The rate constant is k and it links the rate of reaction to the concentration of the reactants in the rate equation.
- The order of reaction with respect to a specific reactant is determined experimentally by measuring the rate of reaction against known concentrations of this reactant.
- The overall order of reaction is the sum of the individual orders of reaction.
- A reactant with an order of zero does not take part in the rate-determining step in the reaction.

Examiner tip

From AS2 you should know that a 'dynamic equilibrium' is an equilibrium in which both the forward and reverse reactions are occurring at the same rate and the concentration of reactants and products remains constant.

Examiner tip

K_c and K_p can both be calculated for homogeneous gaseous equilibria as the concentration of a gas can be calculated as the number of moles of the gas in a certain volume (in dm^3).

Equilibrium

The equilibrium laws

K represents the equilibrium constant. The subscript letter after K shows what type of equilibrium is being expressed. K_c is an equilibrium constant calculated from **c**oncentrations of reactants and products (in $mol\,dm^{-3}$). K_p is an equilibrium constant calculated from partial **p**ressure of reactants and products (measured in pressure units) for homogeneous gaseous reactions.

All equilibrium constants are only constant at constant temperature. The temperature should be quoted when the value of any equilibrium constant is given. If temperature remains constant the equilibrium constant will not change. If any other factor is varied, such as pressure or concentration of reactants, the value of the equilibrium constant does not change.

K_c

For the reaction:

$$aA + bB \rightleftharpoons cC + dD$$

$$K_c = \frac{[C]^c[D]^d}{[A]^a[B]^b}$$

where [C] represents the concentration of C in $mol\,dm^{-3}$ in the equilibrium mixture and c is the balancing number for C in the equation for the reaction. The same applies to A, B and D. The concentrations of all products at equilibrium are on the top line of the expression raised to the power of their balancing numbers and the concentrations of all reactants at equilibrium are on the bottom line, again raised to the power of their balancing numbers.

Concentration is often calculated as the number of moles of a reactant or products divided by the volume (most often in dm^3).

Units of K_c are $\dfrac{(mol\,dm^{-3})^{(c+d)}}{(mol\,dm^{-3})^{(a+b)}}$

The units are in terms of concentration, in $mol\,dm^{-3}$, but the overall power depends on the balancing numbers in the equation for the reaction.

K_p

For the reaction:

$$aA(g) + bB(g) \rightleftharpoons cC(g) + dD(g)$$

$$K_p = \frac{(pC)^c(pD)^d}{(pA)^a(pB)^b}$$

where pC represents the **partial pressure** of C in the equilibrium mixture and c is the balancing number for C in the equation for the reaction. The same applies to A, B and D. The partial pressures of all products are on the top line of the expression raised to the power of their balancing numbers and the partial pressures of all reactants are on the bottom line again raised to the power of their balancing numbers.

The mole fraction is the number of moles of that particular gas at equilibrium divided by the total number of moles of all gases at equilibrium:

$$mole\ fraction = \frac{number\ of\ moles\ of\ a\ particular\ gas\ at\ equilibrium}{total\ number\ of\ moles\ of\ gas\ at\ equilibrium}$$

The units of partial pressure are the same as units of the overall pressure.

Units of K_p are $\dfrac{(pressure\ unit)^{(c+d)}}{(pressure\ unit)^{(a+b)}}$

The units of K_p depend on the units of the partial pressure.

Writing K_c and K_p expressions and calculation of units

Questions commonly ask you to write an expression for K_c or K_p and to calculate the units of K_c or K_p.

Examiner tip

This is very important. The position of equilibrium may vary when external factors are changed but only changes in temperature will affect the value of the equilibrium constant. This is a common question.

The **partial pressure** is the mole fraction of a gas in the equilibrium mixture multiplied by the total pressure of the system:

partial pressure = mole fraction × total pressure

Examiner tip

The total of all the mole fractions should add up to 1. The total of the partial pressures should add up to the total pressure. This is a handy check if you are asked to calculate the mole fractions and then the partial pressures.

Worked example 1

Write an expression for K_c for the reaction:

$$PCl_5 \rightleftharpoons PCl_3 + Cl_2$$

and calculate its units.

$$K_c = \frac{[PCl_3][Cl_2]}{[PCl_5]} \qquad \text{Units of } K_c = \frac{(\text{mol dm}^{-3})^2}{(\text{mol dm}^{-3})} = \text{mol dm}^{-3}$$

Worked example 2

Write an expression for K_p for the reaction:

$$N_2(g) + 3H_2(g) \rightleftharpoons 2NH_3(g)$$

and calculate its units when the total pressure is measured in atm (atmospheres).

$$K_p = \frac{(pNH_3)^2}{(pN_2)(pH_2)^3} \qquad \text{Units of } K_p = \frac{(\text{atm})^2}{(\text{atm})^4} = \text{atm}^{-2}$$

Worked example 3

Write an expression for K_c for the reaction:

$$CH_3COOH + CH_3CH_2OH \rightleftharpoons CH_3COOCH_2CH_3 + H_2O$$

and state any units.

$$K_c = \frac{[CH_3COOCH_2CH_3][H_2O]}{[CH_3COOH][CH_3CH_2OH]} \qquad \text{Units of } K_c = \frac{(\text{mol dm}^{-3})^2}{(\text{mol dm}^{-3})^2} = \text{no units}$$

No units of K_c and K_p

For the general reaction $A + B \rightleftharpoons C + D$:

$$K_c = \frac{[C][D]}{[A][B]} \qquad \text{Units} = \frac{(\text{mol dm}^{-3})^2}{(\text{mol dm}^{-3})^2} = \text{no units}$$

If K_c has no units, then the total volume in the reaction will not make a difference to the calculation of K_c. This means that the number of moles at equilibrium can be used instead of concentration at equilibrium in the K_c expression. This is important if the volume in which the reaction occurs is not given to you. The same applies to the total pressure if K_p has no units; mole fractions at equilibrium can be used instead of partial pressures in the K_p expression.

Calculating K_c and using K_c

The calculations involving K_c may involve calculating K_c or using K_c to calculate an equilibrium number of moles or an initial number of moles or a concentration at equilibrium.

Calculating K_c

The general format in Table 5 is followed to calculate number of moles of each substance at equilibrium.

Table 5

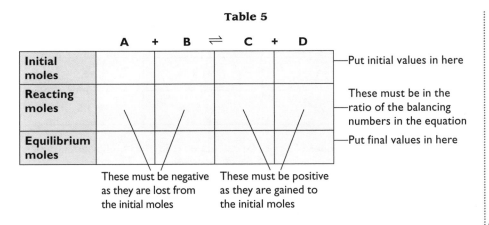

These must be negative as they are lost from the initial moles

These must be positive as they are gained to the initial moles

Worked example I

Calculate K_c for the reaction below at a certain temperature if 5 mol of nitrogen monoxide give 1.5 mol of nitrogen at equilibrium.

$$2NO(g) \rightleftharpoons N_2(g) + O_2(g)$$

$$K_c = \frac{[N_2][O_2]}{[NO]^2}$$
Units of $K_c = \frac{(mol\,dm^{-3})^2}{(mol\,dm^{-3})^2}$ = no units

The first step is to fill in the number of moles you are given. (Note as there is only NO present initially — the initial moles of N_2 and O_2 are both zero.)

	2NO $\rightleftharpoons$	N_2 +	O_2
Initial moles	5	0	0
Reacting moles			
Equilibrium moles		1.5	

The second step is to calculate the other number of moles of each substance present at equilibrium. If 1.5 mol of N_2 are formed the reacting moles of N_2 are +1.5. This means that the reacting moles of NO are −3 (based on the ratio in the equation) and the reacting moles of O_2 are +1.5.

	2NO $\rightleftharpoons$	N_2 +	O_2
Initial moles	5	0	0
Reacting moles	−3	+1.5	+1.5
Equilibrium moles		1.5	

The next step is to complete the equilibrium number of moles of each substance. For NO it is 5 − 3 = 2 mol. For O_2 it is 0 + 1.5 = 1.5 mol.

	2NO	$\rightleftharpoons$	**N$_2$**	+	**O$_2$**
Initial moles	5		0		0
Reacting moles	−3		+1.5		+1.5
Equilibrium moles	2		1.5		1.5

As K_c has no units, the values of K_c can be calculated from the equilibrium number of moles.

$$K_c = \frac{[N_2][O_2]}{[NO]^2} = \frac{1.5 \times 1.5}{2^2} = \frac{1.5^2}{2^2} = 0.5625 \text{ (no units)}$$

Calculating K_c from concentrations

The concentrations of the reactants initially may be given as concentrations or number of moles in a specific volume. For a K_c that has units, the calculation of K_c must use concentration values (in $mol\,dm^{-3}$). Carry out the calculation as before but determine the equilibrium concentrations by dividing the equilibrium moles by the volume (which will be given in the question).

Worked example 2

Nitrogen reacts with hydrogen according to the reaction:

$$N_2(g) + 3H_2(g) \rightleftharpoons 2NH_3(g)$$

0.025 mol of nitrogen are mixed with 0.010 mol of hydrogen in a volume of 2 dm^3 at 150°C and at equilibrium the number of moles of ammonia is $6.36 \times 10^{-5}\,mol\,dm^{-3}$. Determine the value of the equilibrium constant, K_c, at 150°C.

	N$_2$	+	**3H$_2$**	$\rightleftharpoons$	**2NH$_3$**
Initial moles	0.025		0.01		0
Reacting moles					
Equilibrium moles					6.36×10^{-5}
Equilibrium concentration					

Calculating the number of equilibrium moles as before:

	N$_2$	+	**3H$_2$**	$\rightleftharpoons$	**2NH$_3$**
Initial moles	0.025		0.01		0
Reacting moles	-3.18×10^{-5}		-9.54×10^{-5}		$+6.36 \times 10^{-5}$
Equilibrium moles	0.02497		9.905×10^{-3}		6.36×10^{-5}
Equilibrium concentration					

Equilibrium concentrations are calculated by dividing the number of equilibrium moles by the volume ($2\,dm^3$).

	N_2 +	$3H_2$ ⇌	$2NH_3$
Initial moles	0.025	0.01	0
Reacting moles	-3.18×10^{-5}	-9.54×10^{-5}	$+6.36 \times 10^{-5}$
Equilibrium moles	0.02497	9.905×10^{-3}	6.36×10^{-5}
Equilibrium concentration	0.012485	4.953×10^{-3}	3.18×10^{-5}

$$K_c = \frac{[NH_3]^2}{[N_2][H_2]^3} = \frac{(3.18 \times 10^{-5})^2}{(0.012485) \times (4.953 \times 10^{-3})^3} = \frac{1.011 \times 10^{-9}}{1.517 \times 10^{-9}}$$

$$= 0.6664\,mol^{-2}\,dm^6$$

Examiner tip
The answer here is calculated from the rounded values in the table and in the K_c expression. Show each step in a calculation carefully, so that the examiner can see your method.

Worked example 3

The following equilibrium is established at 400°C when 1.0 mol of HI reacts.

$$2HI(g) \rightleftharpoons H_2(g) + I_2(g)$$

It is found that the HI has undergone 22% dissociation.

Write an expression for the equilibrium constant, K_c. Use this to calculate the value of the equilibrium constant at 400°C and state its units.

$$K_c = \frac{[HI]^2}{[H_2][I_2]}$$

22% dissociation means that 22% of the 1 mol of HI reacts. So 0.22 mol of HI reacts. There are no units of this K_c value, so the volume is not required and equilibrium moles can be used to calculate K_c.

	$2HI$ ⇌	H_2 +	I_2
Initial moles	1	0	0
Reacting moles	-0.22	$+0.11$	$+0.11$
Equilibrium moles	0.78	0.11	0.11

$$K_c = \frac{[HI]^2}{[H_2][I_2]} = \frac{(0.11)(0.11)}{(0.78)^2} = 0.0199 \text{ (no units)}$$

Calculations using K_c

Questions may ask you to use a K_c value to determine a concentration or number of moles of a reactant or product at equilibrium.

If K_c is given, then the values are completed in terms of x where x is the number of moles of a substance that reacts ($-x$ in the concentration reacting box for substance A).

The equilibrium number of moles of the other substances are determined using the balancing numbers in the equation.

Table 6 shows the values if initial moles of A and B are 1.

Table 6

	A	+	B	⇌	C	+	D
Initial concentration (or moles)	1		1		0		0
Reacting concentration (or moles)	−x		−x		+x		+x
Equilibrium moles	1 − x		1 − x		x		x

K_c is written in terms of x and x is calculated using the given value of K_c.

Worked example 1

For the equilibrium:

$$H_2(g) + I_2(g) \rightleftharpoons 2HI(g)$$

$K_c = 50$ at a certain temperature. Calculate the number of moles of each substance in the equilibrium mixture if initially there are 3 mol of hydrogen and 3 mol of iodine.

$$K_c = \frac{[HI]^2}{[H_2][I_2]} \qquad \text{Units of } K_c = \text{no units}$$

Use x to represent the number of moles of H_2 that reacts, and fill in the values in the usual way in terms of x. The reacting moles of H_2 are $-x$; the reacting moles of I_2 are also $-x$ (1:1 ratio); the reacting moles of HI are $+2x$ (1:2 ratio). This means that the equilibrium moles of each substance are $3 - x$, $3 - x$ and $2x$.

	H₂	+	I₂	⇌	2HI
Initial moles	3		3		0
Reacting moles	−x		−x		+2x
Equilibrium moles	3 − x		3 − x		2x

$$K_c = \frac{[HI]^2}{[H_2][I_2]} = \frac{(2x)^2}{(3-x)^2} = 50$$

$$\left(\frac{2x}{(3-x)}\right)^2 = 50 \quad \text{so} \quad \frac{2x}{(3-x)} = \sqrt{50} \quad \text{so} \quad \frac{2x}{(3-x)} = 7.07$$

$$2x = 7.07(3-x) \quad \text{so} \quad 2x = 21.21 - 7.07x$$

$$9.07x = 21.21 \quad \text{so} \quad x = 2.34$$

equilibrium number of moles $H_2 = 0.66$; $I_2 = 0.66$; $HI = 4.68$

If the equilibrium concentration of HI in a volume of 10 dm³ was asked for, then the concentration would be $4.68/10 = 0.468 \, \text{mol dm}^{-3}$.

Examiner tip

As there are no units of K_c, there is no need to use a volume to determine concentration. If a volume is given you can ignore it unless you are asked for equilibrium concentration of a substance. Then you must divide the equilibrium moles that you calculated by the volume (in dm³).

Examiner tip

When carrying out this method it is important to take square roots so that there is not a quadratic equation to solve. The specification states that the solution of a quadratic equation is not required, so only this type of calculation can be given where K_c has no units.

Worked example 2

In the following reaction:

$$CO_2(g) + H_2(g) \rightleftharpoons H_2O(g) + CO(g)$$

$K_c = 0.955$ at $1000\,K$. If 1 mol of CO_2 and 1 mol of H_2 are mixed in a total volume of $2.5\,dm^3$, calculate the concentration of $CO_2(g)$ present at equilibrium.

	$CO_2(g)$	+	$H_2(g)$	$\rightleftharpoons$	$H_2O(g)$	+	$CO(g)$
Initial concentration (or moles)	1		1		0		0
Reacting concentration (or moles)	$-x$		$-x$		$+x$		$+x$
Equilibrium concentration (or moles)	$1 - x$		$1 - x$		x		x

$$K_c = \frac{[H_2O][CO]}{[CO_2][H_2]} = \frac{(x)^2}{(1-x)^2} = 0.955$$

$$\left(\frac{x}{(1-x)}\right)^2 = 0.955 \quad \text{so} \quad \frac{x}{(1-x)} = \sqrt{0.955} \quad \text{so} \quad \frac{x}{(1-x)} = 0.977$$

$$x = 0.977 - 0.977x \quad \text{so} \quad x + 0.977x = 0.977$$

$$1.977x = 0.977 \quad \text{so} \quad x = \frac{0.977}{1.977} = 0.4942$$

Since $x = 0.4942$ in this equilibrium mixture, the number of moles of CO_2 present at equilibrium is $1 - x = 1 - 0.4942 = 0.5058$.

The equilibrium concentration of CO_2 is the number of moles divided by the volume $= \dfrac{0.5058}{2.5} = 0.2023\,mol\,dm^{-3}$.

Examiner tip

Since this K_c value has no units, the value of the moles at equilibrium can be determined from the equilibrium moles at equilibrium in terms of x. The concentration is then determined using the volume.

Mole fractions and partial pressures

For homogeneous gaseous reactions, partial pressures can be used to calculate a value for K_p. Partial pressures are calculated from mole fractions and total pressure of the system.

For the reaction:

$$A(g) + B(g) \rightleftharpoons C(g) + D(g)$$

$$\text{mole fraction of A} = \frac{\text{total number of moles of gas A at equilibrium}}{\text{total number of moles of gas at equilibrium}} = x_A$$

$$\text{mole fraction of B} = \frac{\text{total number of moles of gas B at equilibrium}}{\text{total number of moles of gas at equilibrium}} = x_B$$

$$\text{mole fraction of C} = \frac{\text{total number of moles of gas C at equilibrium}}{\text{total number of moles of gas at equilibrium}} = x_C$$

$$\text{mole fraction of D} = \frac{\text{total number of moles of gas D at equilibrium}}{\text{total number of moles of gas at equilibrium}} = x_D$$

Examiner tip

Remember that the total of the moles fractions must add up to 1. In this general example:

$$x_A + x_B + x_C + x_D = 1$$

Where P is the overall pressure, partial pressures are calculated as shown from the mole fraction. A lower case p followed by the substance is used to represent the partial pressure — for example, the partial pressure of A is pA; the partial pressure of N_2 is pN_2.

$$\text{partial pressure of A } (pA) = x_A \times P$$

$$\text{partial pressure of B } (pB) = x_B \times P$$

$$\text{partial pressure of C } (pC) = x_C \times P$$

$$\text{partial pressure of D } (pD) = x_D \times P$$

For the reaction:

$$A + B \rightleftharpoons C + D$$

$$K_p = \frac{(pC)(pD)}{(pA)(pB)} \qquad \text{Units} = \frac{(\text{pressure})^2}{(\text{pressure})^2} = \text{no units}$$

Examiner tip

Remember that the total of the partial pressures must add to the total pressure. In this general example:

$$pA + pB + pC + pD = P$$

Examiner tip

Remember that if K_p has no units, then K_p can be calculated from mole fractions instead of partial pressures.

Calculating K_p and using K_p

Calculations involving K_p might involve calculating K_p or using K_p to calculate an equilibrium number of moles, a partial pressure, the total pressure on a system or an initial number of moles (Table 7).

Table 7

	A	+	B	$\rightleftharpoons$	C	+	D	
Initial moles								Put initial values in here
Reacting moles								These must be in the ratio of the balancing numbers in the equation, as with K_c
Equilibrium moles								Put final mole values in here
Mole fraction								Calculated from total moles
Partial pressure								Mole fraction × overall pressure

Examiner tip

Initial masses of gases present or even masses of gases present at equilibrium may be given. Simply divide the mass of these gases by the RMM of the gas to determine the initial moles or equilibrium moles and place them into the correct positions in the table. Watch out for the diatomic gases, as you have to use the RMM of the diatomic gas — for example, 32 for O_2.

If K_p is given, then the table is filled in using x as the number of moles of a substance that reacts (for example, $-x$ in the concentration reacting box for A). If K_p is given, the equilibrium moles may be in terms of x when K_p has no units. If you are expected to calculate the total pressure, it can be written as P and the partial pressures will be in terms of P. These can be substituted into the K_p expression and solved for P.

Calculating K_p

Worked example 1

Find K_p for the equilibrium:

$$2SO_2(g) + O_2(g) \rightleftharpoons 2SO_3(g)$$

if an original mixture of 16 g of sulfur dioxide and 4 g of oxygen yields 16 g of sulfur trioxide at equilibrium, at a total pressure of 11 atm and at 450°C.

$$K_p = \frac{p(SO_3)^2}{p(SO_2)^2 p(O_2)} \qquad \text{Units of } K_p = \frac{(atm)^2}{(atm)^2(atm)} = \frac{1}{(atm)} = atm^{-1}$$

From the masses:

$$\text{initial moles of } SO_2 = \frac{16}{64} = 0.25$$

$$\text{initial moles of } O_2 = \frac{4}{32} = 0.125$$

$$\text{equilibrium moles of } SO_3 = \frac{16}{80} = 0.2$$

Completing the table with the given data:

	$2SO_2$	+	O_2	$\rightleftharpoons$	$2SO_3$
Initial moles	0.25		0.125		0
Reacting moles					
Equilibrium moles					0.2
Mole fraction					
Partial pressure					

As with K_c the reacting moles line can be completed. If 0.2 mol of SO_3 are present at equilibrium, then 0.2 mol of SO_2 and 0.1 mol of O_2 must have reacted to form 0.2 mol of SO_3. The table now looks like the one below.

	$2SO_2$	+	O_2	$\rightleftharpoons$	$2SO_3$
Initial moles	0.25		0.125		0
Reacting moles	−0.2		−0.1		+0.2
Equilibrium moles	0.05		0.025		0.2
Mole fraction					
Partial pressure					

The mole fraction is calculated from the total equilibrium moles $= 0.05 + 0.025 + 0.2 = 0.275$. The mole fractions are calculated as shown in the following table.

	2SO$_2$	+	O$_2$	⇌	2SO$_3$
Initial moles	0.25		0.125		0
Reacting moles	−0.2		−0.1		+0.2
Equilibrium moles	0.05		0.025		0.2
Mole fraction	$\frac{0.05}{0.275}$		$\frac{0.05}{0.275}$		$\frac{0.2}{0.275}$
Partial pressure	$\left(\frac{0.05}{0.275}\right) \times 11 = 2$		$\left(\frac{0.025}{0.275}\right) \times 11 = 1$		$\left(\frac{0.2}{0.275}\right) \times 11 = 8$

$$K_p = \frac{p(SO_3)^2}{p(SO_2)^2 p(O_2)} = \frac{8^2}{2^2 \times 1} \times 1 = 16\,\text{atm}^{-1}$$

Calculations using K_p

Worked example 2

For the equilibrium:

$$H_2(g) + I_2(g) \rightleftharpoons 2HI(g)$$

$K_p = 2$ at 1500 K. Initially there is 1 mol of H_2 and 1 mol of I_2. Calculate the number of moles of HI present at equilibrium.

$$K_p = \frac{(pHI)^2}{(pA)(pB)} \qquad \text{Units of } K_p = \frac{(\text{pressure})^2}{(\text{pressure})^2} = \text{no units}$$

As there is 1 mol of H_2 and 1 mol of I_2 present initially, the table can be completed as shown up to the equilibrium moles. This is the same method used for K_c calculations to this point.

	H$_2$	+	I$_2$	⇌	2HI
Initial moles	1		1		0
Reacting moles	−x		−x		+2x
Equilibrium moles	1 − x		1 − x		2x
Mole fraction					
Partial pressure					

The total equilibrium moles of gas are determined:

$$(1 - x) + (1 - x) + 2x = 2$$

The total equilibrium moles of gas is not in terms of x and this is common in this style of question, where K_p has no units. The total pressure is taken as P.

	H_2	+	I_2	$\rightleftharpoons$	$2HI$
Initial moles	1		1		0
Reacting moles	$-x$		$-x$		$+2x$
Equilibrium moles	$1 - x$		$1 - x$		$2x$
Mole fraction	$\dfrac{(1-x)}{2}$		$\dfrac{(1-x)}{2}$		$\dfrac{2x}{2}$
Partial pressure	$\dfrac{(1-x)}{2} \times P$		$\dfrac{(1-x)}{2} \times P$		$\dfrac{2x}{2} \times P$

The mole fractions can be used in place of the partial pressures in the K_p expression as there are no units of K_p. The total pressure, P, would cancel out in the equilibrium expression.

$$K_p = \frac{(pHI)^2}{(pH_2)(pI_2)} = \frac{\left(\frac{2x}{2}\right)^2}{\left(\frac{1-x}{2}\right)^2} = \frac{\frac{(2x)^2}{4}}{\frac{(1-x)^2}{4}} = \frac{(2x)^2}{4} \times \frac{4}{(1-x)^2} = \frac{(2x)^2}{(1-x)^2} = \left(\frac{2x}{1-x}\right)^2$$

$K_p = 2$, so:

$$\left(\frac{2x}{1-x}\right)^2 = 2$$

Taking a square root of both sides:

$$\frac{2x}{1-x} = \sqrt{2} \quad \text{so} \quad \frac{2x}{1-x} = 1.41$$

$$2x = 1.41(1-x) \quad \text{so} \quad 2x = 1.41 - 1.41x$$

$$3.41x = 1.41 \quad \text{so} \quad x = \frac{1.41}{3.41} = 0.414$$

Once the value of x is determined it can be filled into the values in the table to determine mole fractions. If the total pressure is given, the partial pressure can be determined.

	H_2	+	I_2	$\rightleftharpoons$	$2HI$
Equilibrium moles	$1 - x$		$1 - x$		$2x$
When $x = 0.414$	0.586		0.586		0.828

These are the mole fractions, so the answer to the question is that the number of moles of HI present at equilibrium is 0.828.

Examiner tip
This seems complicated maths but it is basically fractions and indices and you will become more proficient with practice. Remember that a fraction divided by another fraction is simply the top fraction multiplied by the bottom fraction upside down. If both quantities in a fraction are squared (top and bottom) then it is a simple fraction, all squared.

Examiner tip
When you have determined the value of x, always check the question to see exactly which quantity you are being asked to determine. It may be $1-x$ or, in this case, it may be $2x$. Many students think they have finished the question when they determine the value of x but the answer may involve using this value further.

Answers to these questions, and those in which we use K_p, can be checked, *if time permits*, by putting your answers into the expression for the equilibrium constant. In this case:

$$K_p = \frac{(0.828)^2}{(0.586)(0.586)} = 2$$

Calculating the total pressure

Often P is used for the total pressure where it has to be determined. You will be given enough information in the question to determine P from the K_p value or sometimes from a partial pressure.

Worked example 3

2 mol of SO_2 and 1 mol of O_2 are mixed and heated to 1000 K. They reach equilibrium according to the equation:

$$2SO_2(g) + O_2(g) \rightleftharpoons 2SO_3(g) \qquad K_p = 0.125\,atm^{-1}$$

A 50% conversion of sulfur dioxide to sulfur trioxide occurs. Determine the total pressure on the system.

$$K_p = \frac{(pSO_3)^2}{(pSO_2)^2(pO_2)} = 0.125\,atm^{-1}$$

	2SO₂	+	O₂	⇌	2SO₃	
Initial moles	2		1		0	If 50% of SO_2 is converted into SO_3 then 1 mol out of the 2 mol of SO_2 reacts
Reacting moles	−1		−0.5		+1	
Equilibrium moles	1		0.5		1	Total equilibrium moles of gas = 2.5
Mole fraction	$\frac{1}{2.5} = 0.4$		$\frac{0.5}{2.5} = 0.2$		$\frac{1}{2.5} = 0.4$	
Partial pressure	0.4P		0.2P		0.4P	

Examiner tip
At this stage $(0.4P)^2$ cancels down to 1 in the expression, leaving $\frac{1}{0.2P}$. You can still multiply out the $(0.4P)^2$ to get $0.16P^2$ but remember that both the 0.4 and the P need to be squared.

$$K_p = \frac{(0.4P)^2}{(0.4P)^2(0.2P)} = \frac{1}{0.2P} = 0.125\,atm^{-1}$$

So:

$$1 = 0.2P \times 0.125$$

$$1 = 0.025P$$

$$P = \frac{1}{0.025} = 40\,atm$$

Position of equilibrium and the equilibrium constant

In AS2 you examined how the **position of equilibrium** changed as the external conditions changed, such as the temperature, pressure, concentration of reactants or products and presence of a catalyst. The changes in the position of equilibrium are explained using Le Chatelier's principle.

Le Chatelier's principle states that if a system in equilibrium is subjected to a change, processes will occur that tend to counteract the change imposed (whenever possible). A change in temperature may result in a change in the position of equilibrium *but will change the value of the equilibrium constant*. A change in concentration or pressure may change the position of equilibrium but will have *no effect* on the value of any equilibrium constant at constant temperature. Remember that a catalyst has no effect on either the position of equilibrium or the value of the equilibrium constant.

Changes in temperature

An exothermic reaction is one in which the forward reaction releases energy in the form of heat.

- Increasing the temperature of an exothermic reaction will favour the reverse endothermic reaction (to absorb heat) and so the position of equilibrium will move to the left and the value of the equilibrium constant will be less.
- Increasing the temperature of an endothermic reaction will favour the forward endothermic reaction (to absorb heat) and so the position of equilibrium will move to the right and the value of the equilibrium constant will be greater.

Examiner tip

Equilibrium constants are constant at a given temperature. Only a change in temperature affects the value of any equilibrium constant: K_c, K_p, K_d, K_a, K_w and any other K values you will meet.

Examiner tip

This information can be used to predict whether a reaction is exothermic or endothermic based on the values of the equilibrium constant at different temperatures.

Worked example

The reaction between hydrogen and bromine is represented by the equation:

$$H_2(g) + Br_2(g) \rightleftharpoons 2HBr(g)$$

K_c values for this reaction at different temperatures are:

Temperature / K	K_c
300	1.0×10^{17}
500	1.3×10^{10}
1000	3.8×10^4

Is the reaction endothermic or exothermic? Explain your answer.

K_c is affected by changes in temperature. As the temperature increases, the value of K_c decreases. This means that the concentration of reactants has increased at higher temperatures so the reverse reaction is endothermic. Therefore the forward reaction is exothermic.

Changes in concentration

Changes in concentration will affect the position of equilibrium but they will have no effect on the value of the equilibrium constant. The equilibrium will re-establish itself with new concentrations to give the same value for the equilibrium constant providing the temperature remains constant.

- Increasing the concentration of a reactant (adding more of a reactant) will move the position of equilibrium to the right. This will have no effect on the value of the equilibrium constant.
- Removing a product from the reaction (by further reaction) will also move the position of equilibrium to the right to replace the removed product, but again this will have no effect on the equilibrium constant.

• Increasing the concentration of a product (by adding more of it) will move the position of equilibrium to the left-hand side but again this has no effect on the value of the equilibrium constant.

Changes in pressure

The effect of pressure on the position of equilibrium is determined by the numbers of moles of gases on each side of the equation. A higher number of moles of gas means a greater volume.

• An increase in pressure favours a smaller gas volume so will move the position of equilibrium to the side with the smaller number of moles of gas.
• A decrease in pressure favours a larger gas volume so will move the position of equilibrium to the side with the larger number of moles of gas.
• Any equilibrium constant, including K_p, is *not affected* by changes in pressure.

Effect of adding a catalyst

Adding a catalyst to a system at equilibrium has *no effect* on the composition of the equilibrium mixture and has *no effect* on the position of equilibrium or the equilibrium constant.

Most of the changes mentioned in the last section also affect the rate at which equilibrium is established. Increasing the temperature speeds up both the forward and backward reactions and so equilibrium is attained more quickly regardless of whether the equilibrium shifts to the right or the left. If the position of equilibrium shifts to left it does so because the backward reaction is speeded up more than the forward reaction. Likewise equilibrium is attained faster if we increase the pressure (of a homogeneous gaseous equilibrium) or add a catalyst.

K_d

K_d is the partition coefficient (sometimes called the distribution coefficient). It is the ratio of the concentration of a solute between two immiscible solvents, which form distinct layers.

The expression for K_d is:

$$K_d = \frac{\text{[solute in upper layer at equilibrium]}}{\text{[solute in lower layer at equilibrium]}}$$

where [solute] represents concentration of the solute.

For example, the partition coefficient of solute X between ether and water is 4.

$$K_d = \frac{\text{[solute X in ether]}}{\text{[solute X in water]}} = 4.0$$

Solvents that do not mix with water are, for example, hexane (C_6H_{14}), ether ($CH_3CH_2OCH_2CH_3$) and tetrachloromethane (CCl_4). They are all non-polar solvents or organic solvents.

Knowledge check 8

What effect does increasing the pressure have on the position of equilibrium and K_p for the reaction:

$N_2(g) + 3H_2(g) \rightleftharpoons 2NH_3(g)$

where $\Delta H = -92.2\,kJ$?

Examiner tip

K_d is written as the partition coefficient of the solute between solvent 1 and solvent 2 — solvent 1 is on the top of the expression, as it is stated first. This is the concentration in the upper (less dense) layer divided by the concentration in the lower (denser layer), but follow the order given in the text. You may be given the expression for K_d.

Examiner tip

The partition coefficient of solute X between water and ether is the reciprocal = 1/4.0 = 0.25, so:

$K_d = \frac{\text{[solute X in water]}}{\text{[solute X in ether]}}$

= 0.25

Ether is less dense than water so the first expression is preferred chemically, but the second may be used if the order is stated, i.e. between water and ether.

Solvent extraction

Organic substances can be extracted from an aqueous solution using a non-polar solvent:

1 Mix the aqueous solution with a certain volume of the *named* non-polar solvent.
2 Place in a separating funnel, stopper and shake.
3 Invert and open the tap to release any pressure caused by a volatile non-polar solvent.
4 Allow to settle and remove stopper.
5 Run off the bottom layer (usually the aqueous layer).
6 Add more solvent to the aqueous layer and repeat.
7 Combine the organic layers and evaporate the solvent (without heat) to obtain solids.

Solvent extraction works on the principle that certain solutes are more soluble in non-polar solvents than in water and so more will dissolve in the non-polar organic layer in the separating funnel. Solvent extraction works better (i.e. extracts more solute) when the volume of organic solvent is split into smaller portions and multiple extractions are carried out.

Determining K_d practically

1 A solute X is dissolved in either water or an organic solvent (volume will be given).
2 Add a certain known volume of other solvent (organic or water, respectively).
3 Shake and allow to settle.
4 Titrate samples of each layer for solute X and determine concentration (or use colorimetry if coloured, with a calibration curve to determine concentration).
5 From here the concentrations of the solute in both layers can be determined and K_d calculated.

Using K_d

K_d has no units as it is simply the concentration of a solute in one solvent divided by the concentration of the same solute in a different solvent.

Examiner tip

Because K_d has no units, various units can be used for the concentrations such as $mol\,dm^{-3}$, $g\,dm^{-3}$, $g\,cm^{-3}$ (most common in calculations). The number of moles or $mol\,dm^{-3}$ does not need to be calculated as the substance on the top and bottom of the K_d expression is the same, so has the same RFM/RMM. Any measurement of mass or moles per unit volume is acceptable for the units of concentration.

The calculations are best carried out using a table such as Table 8.

Table 8

	Solute A in aqueous solvent, A(aq)	Solute A in organic solvent, A(org)	
Initial mass			Mass of solute A initially in each solvent (usually one of these is 0)
Equilibrium mass			Mass based on *x* moles of solute A moving from one solvent to another
Volume of solvent			Volume of each solvent is given in the question
Equilibrium concentration			Equilibrium mass divided by volume of solvent

$$K_d = \frac{[A]_{solvent\,1}}{[A]_{solvent\,2}}$$

where [A] represents the concentration of A.

Calculating mass extracted

Worked example

The partition coefficient of A between ether and water is 4.0.

5 g of A were dissolved in 100 cm³ of water and mixed with 10 cm³ of ether. Calculate the mass extracted into the ether.

	Solute A in aqueous solvent, A(aq)	Solute A in organic solvent, A(org)
Initial mass	5	0
Equilibrium mass	$5 - x$	x
Volume of solvent	100	10
Equilibrium concentration	$\dfrac{(5-x)}{100}$	$\dfrac{x}{10}$

Examiner tip

Remember to watch for whether the mass of solute remaining or that of the solvent extracted is asked for. In this example it could be the mass extracted into the ether (x) or the mass that remains in the water ($5 - x$) as both will be given in a multiple-choice question.

$$K_d = \frac{[A]_{ether}}{[A]_{water}} = \frac{\dfrac{x}{10}}{\dfrac{(5-x)}{100}} = 4.0$$

$$\frac{x}{10} = \frac{4(5-x)}{100}$$

$$100x = 200 - 40x$$

$$140x = 200$$

$$x = \frac{200}{140} = 1.43$$

The value of x is 1.43 so the mass that is dissolved in the ether at equilibrium is x g. Therefore the mass extracted is 1.43 g.

Calculating K_d

You may be told the mass in each layer or the concentration in each layer and be expected to work out the value of K_d.

Worked example

Calculate the partition coefficient between ether and water for X based on the equilibrium shown on the left.

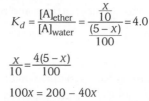

20 cm³ of ether containing 6 g of X

10 cm³ of water containing 4 g of X

	Solute X in aqueous solvent, X(aq)	Solute X in organic solvent, X(org)
Equilibrium mass	4	6
Volume of solvent	10	20
Equilibrium concentration	$\dfrac{4}{10} = 0.4$	$\dfrac{6}{20} = 0.3$

$$K_d = \frac{[X]_{ether}}{[X]_{water}} = \frac{0.3}{0.4} = 0.75$$

Multiple extractions (solvent extraction)

To extract the maximum mass of solute, the solvent is divided into smaller portions and multiple extractions carried out. Two portions of $10\,cm^3$ of an organic solvent will extract more than one $20\,cm^3$ portion. Simply carry out the calculation twice using the mass remaining in the water after the first extraction as the starting mass of solute for the second calculation.

- $K_c = \dfrac{[C]^c[D]^d}{[A]^a[B]^b}$ for the reaction

  $aA + bB \rightleftharpoons cC + dD.$

- $[A]$ represents the concentration of A in $mol\,dm^{-3}$.
- The units of K_c depend on the values of a, b, c and d.
- $K_p = \dfrac{(pC)^c\,(pD)^d}{(pA)^a\,(pB)^b}$ for the gaseous equilibrium

  $aA + bB \rightleftharpoons cC + dD.$

- pA represents the partial pressure of gas A in the mixture and is calculated from the mole fraction of A × total pressure.
- The units of K_p are in pressure units or can be no units depending on a, b, c and d.
- K_d has no units; it is the concentration of a substance in the upper layer divided by the concentration of the same substance in the lower layer.

Acid–base equilibria

Brønsted theory of acids and bases

The Brønsted definition of acids and bases depends on protons. A hydrogen ion, H^+, is a proton so the term hydrogen ion and proton are interchangeable.

In the following reaction:

$$NH_3 + H_2O \rightleftharpoons NH_4^+ + OH^-$$

- NH_3 accepts a proton to become NH_4^+. NH_3 acts as a Brønsted base.
- H_2O donates a proton. H_2O acts as a Brønsted acid.
- NH_3 and NH_4^+ are a conjugate acid–base pair, as are H_2O and OH^-.
- NH_4^+ is the conjugate acid of NH_3 as NH_4^+ can donate a proton in the reverse reaction to reform NH_3.
- OH^- is the conjugate base of H_2O as OH^- can accept a proton in the reverse reaction to reform H_2O.

In the following reaction:

$$CH_3COOH + H_2O \rightleftharpoons CH_3COO^- + H_3O^+$$

- H_2O accepts a proton to become H_3O^+. H_2O acts as a Brønsted base.
- CH_3COOH donates a proton. CH_3COOH acts as a Brønsted acid.
- CH_3COOH and CH_3COO^- are a conjugate acid–base pair, as are H_2O and H_3O^+.
- H_3O^+ is the conjugate acid of H_2O as H_3O^+ can donate a proton in the reverse reaction to reform H_2O.
- CH_3COO^- is the conjugate base of CH_3COOH as CH_3COO^- can accept a proton in the reverse reaction to reform CH_3COOH.

A **Brønsted acid** is defined as a proton donor. A **Brønsted base** is defined as a proton acceptor.

Examiner tip

Water can act as both a Brønsted acid and base. Other species can do this as well, such as the hydrogenphosphate ion, HPO_4^{2-}, dihydrogenphosphate ion, $H_2PO_4^-$ and the hydrogencarbonate ion, HCO_3^-.

H_3O^+ is the hydronium ion (or hydroxonium ion or oxonium ion). It is the ion formed when acids react with water. All three names are acceptable.

Knowledge check 9

What is the conjugate base of water?

Classification of acids and bases

Acids (and bases) may be classified as strong or weak depending on the degree to which they are dissociated in solution.

A **strong acid** is fully dissociated into its ions in solution. For example:

$$HCl \rightarrow H^+ + Cl^-$$

$$H_2SO_4 \rightarrow 2H^+ + SO_4^{2-}$$

$$HNO_3 \rightarrow H^+ + NO_3^-$$

HCl and HNO_3 are described as monobasic acids. H_2SO_4 is a dibasic acid.

A **weak acid** is partially dissociated into its ions in solution. For example:

$$CH_3COOH \rightleftharpoons H^+ + CH_3COO^-$$

$$HNO_2 \rightleftharpoons H^+ + NO_2^-$$

Generally this can be represented as:

$$HA \rightleftharpoons H^+ + A^-$$

where HA is the undissociated monobasic acid.

Strong bases are fully dissociated into their ions in solution whereas weak bases are partially dissociated into their ions in solution.

Group I hydroxides are strong bases, for example sodium hydroxide (NaOH) and potassium hydroxide (KOH). Ammonia is the most common example of a weak base.

$$NaOH \rightarrow Na^+ + OH^-$$

$$KOH \rightarrow K^+ + OH^-$$

$$NH_3 + H_2O \rightleftharpoons NH_4^+ + OH^-$$

Soluble bases are called alkalis and they form hydroxide ions in solution.

Calculating pH

pH (always written with a small p and a capital H) is a logarithmic scale that gives a measure of the H^+ concentration in a solution. Neutral solutions have a pH value

CCEA A2 Chemistry

of 7.0. Acidic solutions have a pH of less than 7 and alkaline solutions have a pH of greater than 7. An alkali is a soluble base and when bases dissociate in solution they are called alkalis.

$$pH = -\log_{10}[H^+] \quad \text{or more simply} \quad pH = -\log[H^+]$$

where [H$^+$] represents the concentration of H$^+$ ions in solution measured in mol dm^{-3} (or M).

To calculate the hydrogen ion concentration from the pH, reverse the calculation:

$$[H^+] = \text{antilog}(-pH)$$

Examiner tip

log$_{10}$ is the standard log button on your calculator. Antilog may appear as 10^x on your calculator and you may have to use shift log to access the function. Try a few calculations to make sure you can convert from [H$^+$] to pH and from pH to [H$^+$].

pH of strong acids

Figure 15 shows the links between concentration of the acid, [acid], concentration of hydrogen ions, [H$^+$], and pH for a strong acid.

Knowledge check 10

Define pH.

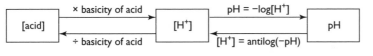

Figure 15

Calculating pH of strong acids

Worked example 1

Calculate the pH of 0.05 M hydrochloric acid.

For strong monobasic acids the basicity is 1, so [H$^+$] = 1 × [acid].

$$HCl \rightarrow H^+ + Cl^-$$

If [HCl] = 0.05 M then [H$^+$] = 0.05 M.

$$pH = -\log[H^+] = -\log(0.05) = 1.3$$

Worked example 2

Calculate the pH of 1.0 mol dm^{-3} sulfuric acid.

For strong dibasic acids the basicity is 2, so [H$^+$] = 2 × [acid].

$$H_2SO_4 \rightarrow 2H^+ + SO_4^{2-}$$

If [H$_2$SO$_4$] = 1.0 then [H$^+$] = 2.0 mol dm^{-3}.

$$pH = -\log[H^+] = -\log(2) = -0.3$$

Examiner tip

pH values are normally given between 0 and 14 but values below 0 are possible for very high [H$^+$]. Values above 14 are also possible for very high [OH$^-$].

Determining the concentration of an acid from its pH

If you are given the pH of a strong acid you can calculate the concentration of the hydrogen ions and so the concentration of the acid.

Worked example 3

(a) Determine the concentration of nitric acid that has a pH of 0.7.

$$[H^+] = antilog(-pH) = antilog(-0.7) = 0.2\,M$$

Nitric acid (HNO_3) is a strong monobasic acid, so the [acid] = [H^+].

concentration of nitric acid = 0.2 M

(b) Determine the concentration of sulfuric acid that has a pH of 1.0.

$$[H^+] = antilog(-pH) = antilog(-1) = 0.1\,M$$

Sulfuric acid (H_2SO_4) is a strong dibasic acid, so the [acid] $= \dfrac{[H^+]}{2} = \dfrac{0.1}{2} = 0.05\,M$.

concentration of sulfuric acid = 0.05 M

Ionic product of water

Water partially dissociates into hydrogen ions and hydroxide ions:

$$H_2O \rightleftharpoons H^+ + OH^-$$

- K_w is the ionic product of water and $K_w = [H^+][OH^-]$.
- Units of K_w are always $mol^2\,dm^{-6}$.
- At 25.0°C, $K_w = 1.0 \times 10^{-14}\,mol^2\,dm^{-6}$.

Examiner tip

We have become accustomed to thinking that the pH of pure water is 7 but this is only true at 25°C. As temperature increases above 25°C, the pH of water drops below 7. The increase in K_w as temperature increases also indicates that the dissociation of water into H^+ and OH^- ions is endothermic, because the equilibrium is moving to the right (more H^+) as temperature increases.

Calculating the pH of pure water

In pure water [H^+] = [OH^-], so $K_w = [H^+]^2$.

Worked example

K_w at 25°C is $1.0 \times 10^{-14}\,mol^2\,dm^{-6}$, whereas at 40°C $K_w = 2.92 \times 10^{-14}\,mol^2\,dm^{-6}$. Calculate the pH of water at 25°C and at 40°C.

At 25°C:

$$K_w = 1.0 \times 10^{-14} = [H^+]^2$$

$$[H^+] = \sqrt{1.0 \times 10^{-14}} = 1.0 \times 10^{-7}\,mol\,dm^{-3}$$

$$pH = -\log[H^+] = -\log(1.0 \times 10^{-7}) = 7$$

At 40°C:

$$K_w = 2.92 \times 10^{-14} = [H^+]^2$$

$$[H^+] = \sqrt{2.92 \times 10^{-14}} = 1.71 \times 10^{-7}\,mol\,dm^{-3}$$

$$pH = -\log[H^+] = -\log(1.71 \times 10^{-7}) = 6.77$$

Knowledge check 11

Calculate the pH of 0.2 M sulfuric acid.

pH of strong alkalis

An alkali is a soluble base. When a soluble base dissolves in water, hydroxide ions are present in the solution. The concentration of the hydroxide ions, $[OH^-]$, can be related to the $[H^+]$ using K_w because at 25°C $K_w = 1.0 \times 10^{-14} \, mol^2 \, dm^{-6}$.

In pure water $[H^+] = [OH^-]$, but this is not true in acid or alkaline solutions. K_w and $[OH^-]$ can be used to calculate $[H^+]$, which is then used to determine pH.

Figure 16 shows the links between concentration of the alkali, [alkali], concentration of hydroxide ions, $[OH^-]$, concentration of hydrogen ions, $[H^+]$, and pH for a strong alkali.

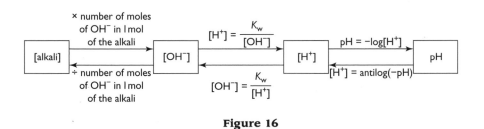

Figure 16

Calculating the pH of a strong alkali

Worked example 1

Calculate the pH of a 0.25 M solution of sodium hydroxide ($K_w = 1.0 \times 10^{-14} \, mol^2 \, dm^{-6}$). Sodium hydroxide is a strong base and so dissociates fully in solution:

$$NaOH \rightarrow Na^+ + OH^-$$

Also 1 mol of sodium hydroxide contains 1 mol of OH^- ions.

$$[\text{alkali}] = 0.25 \, M \quad so \quad [OH^-] = 0.25 \, M$$

$$[H^+] = \frac{K_w}{[OH^-]} = \frac{1.0 \times 10^{-14}}{0.25} \quad so \quad [H^+] = 4 \times 10^{-14} \, M$$

$$pH = -\log(4 \times 10^{-14}) = 13.4$$

Calculating the concentration of an alkali from its pH

Worked example 2

Calculate the concentration in $g \, dm^{-3}$ of potassium hydroxide solution with a pH of 12.5.

$$[H^+] = \text{antilog}(-pH) = \text{antilog}(-12.5) = 3.16 \times 10^{-13} \, M$$

$$[OH^-] = \frac{K_w}{[H^+]} = \frac{1.0 \times 10^{-14}}{3.16 \times 10^{-13}} = 0.032 \, M$$

Potassium hydroxide (KOH) has 1 mol of OH^- ions per mole of base (alkali), so the concentration of KOH, [KOH] = 0.032 M.

$$\text{concentration in } g \, dm^{-3} = 0.032 \times 56 = 1.792 \, g \, dm^{-3}$$

Examiner tip
Concentration is measured in $mol \, dm^{-3}$ but this can be expressed as molarity (M) where 1 $mol \, dm^{-3}$ is equal to 1 M.

Examiner tip
The majority of strong bases (alkalis) you will encounter will have 1 mol of OH^- ions per mole of the base. However, sometimes a question is set on a Group II hydroxide where you are asked to assume that the base is strong, and so the number of moles of OH^- per mole of base is 2.

pK_w, pH and pOH

$$pK_w = -\log K_w \qquad pK_w = 14 \text{ at } 25°C$$

$$pOH = -\log[OH^-]$$

$$pH + pOH = pK_w$$

Worked example

Calculate the pH of a $2\,g\,dm^{-3}$ solution of sodium hydroxide, NaOH, given that $pK_w = 14$ at 25°C.

RFM of NaOH = 40

concentration of NaOH solution $= \dfrac{2}{40} = 0.05\,mol\,dm^{-3}$

$[OH^-] = 0.05\,mol\,dm^{-3}$

$pOH = -\log[OH^-] = -\log(0.05) = 1.3$

$pK_w = 14 = pOH + pH$

$pH = 14 - 1.3 = 12.7$

pH of weak acids

Examiner tip

HA is the undissociated acid. Remember that the undissociated acid does not cause it to be acidic. It is the concentration of H^+ that causes acidity when the acid dissociates. HA is not acidic until it dissociates. It is important to be able to write K_a expressions for weak acids. It is always the [anion] and [H^+] on the top and [undissociated acid] on the bottom.

Knowledge check 12

Write a K_a expression for ethanoic acid.

Weak acids are partially dissociated in solution. This is represented using a reversible arrow ($\rightleftharpoons$). The equilibrium constant for the acid dissociation is represented by K_a.

For a general acid dissociation HA $\rightleftharpoons H^+ + A^-$:

$$K_a = \frac{[A^-][H^+]}{[HA]}$$

For example:

$$CH_3COOH \rightleftharpoons H^+ + CH_3COO^-$$

$$K_a = \frac{[CH_3COO^-][H^+]}{[CH_3COOH]}$$

K_a always has units of $mol\,dm^{-3}$.

The value of K_a gives a measure of the strength of the acid. A higher K_a value indicates a 'stronger' weak acid. For example, ethanoic acid has a K_a value of $1.8 \times 10^{-5}\,mol\,dm^{-3}$, whereas hydrocyanic acid has a K_a of $4.9 \times 10^{-10}\,mol\,dm^{-3}$.

For a weak acid, [H^+] is calculated from the concentration of the acid and the K_a value.

$$[H^+] = \sqrt{K_a \times \text{initial concentration of acid}}$$

The pH is then calculated using $pH = -\log[H^+]$ (Figure 17).

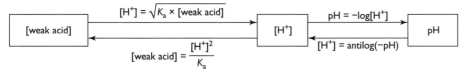

Figure 17

Examiner tip
$[H^+]$ may be determined from pH in the usual way and then the concentration of the weak acid may be calculated using $\frac{[H^+]^2}{K_a}$. This would be an unusual question but still could be asked.

pK_a

The pK_a of a weak acid may be given in place of its K_a. $pK_a = -\log K_a$. To convert between a pK_a value and K_a use the following:

$$K_a = \text{antilog}(-pK_a)$$

The higher the pK_a value, the weaker the acid. A lower pK_a indicates a stronger acid.

Examiner tip
Many questions assume that an acid with several acid groups dissociates once and the calculation is carried out in the normal way. Watch out for dibasic weak acids (such as oxalic acid) and even tribasic weak acids (such as citric acid) as these are treated as weak acids and only the first ionisation of the acid is considered. Just use the method shown for weak acids.

Calculating the pH of a weak acid

Worked example 1

The pK_a for ethanoic acid (CH_3COOH) is 4.745. Calculate the pH of a 0.1 M solution of ethanoic acid.

$$K_a = \text{antilog}(-pK_a) = \text{antilog}(-4.745) = 1.8 \times 10^{-5}\,\text{mol dm}^{-3}$$

$$[H^+] = \sqrt{K_a \times [\text{weak acid}]} = \sqrt{1.8 \times 10^{-5} \times 0.1} = \sqrt{1.8 \times 10^{-6}} = 1.34 \times 10^{-3}\,\text{M}$$

$$pH = -\log[H^+] = -\log(1.34 \times 10^{-3}) = 2.87$$

Calculating the concentration of a weak acid from its pH

Worked example 2

Determine the concentration in $mg\,dm^{-3}$ of a solution of propanoic acid (CH_3CH_2COOH) with a pK_a value of 2.89 and a pH of 2.5.

$$K_a = \text{antilog}(-pK_a) = \text{antilog}(-2.89) = 1.29 \times 10^{-3}\,\text{mol dm}^{-3}$$

$$[H^+] = \text{antilog}(-pH) = \text{antilog}(-2.5) = 3.16 \times 10^{-3}\,\text{mol dm}^{-3}$$

$$[\text{weak acid}] = \frac{[H^+]^2}{K_a} = \frac{(3.16 \times 10^{-3})^2}{1.29 \times 10^{-3}} = 7.74 \times 10^{-3}\,\text{mol dm}^{-3}$$

RMM of propanoic acid (CH_3CH_2COOH) = 74

$$[\text{weak acid}] = 7.74 \times 10^{-3} \times 74 = 0.573\,\text{g dm}^{-3}$$

$$[\text{weak acid}] = 0.573 \times 1000 = 573\,\text{mg dm}^{-3}$$

Examiner tip
The use of unusual units in these types of calculations is common. Remember that there are 1000 (10^3) mg in 1 g and 1 000 000 (10^6) μg in 1 g. The same applies to volume units: 1000 (10^3) ml in 1 litre and 1 000 000 (10^6) μl in 1 litre. 1 cm^3 = 1 ml and 1 dm^3 = 1 litre. These questions are always awkward but knowing the units makes them easier.

Dilutions and neutralisations

When an acid or alkali is neutralised or diluted the concentration of the ions in solution changes. It is important to be able to calculate the new concentration of H^+ or OH^- and then determine the pH of the new solution. The total volume must be taken into account to determine the new concentration in $mol\,dm^{-3}$.

Dilutions

$$\text{concentration of diluted solution (mol dm}^{-3}) = \frac{\text{moles of solute}}{\text{volume of new solution (cm}^3)} \times 1000$$

Worked example 1

20.0 cm³ of a 0.1 M solution of hydrochloric acid are placed in a volumetric flask and the volume made up to 250 cm³ using deionised water. Determine the pH of the resulting solution.

$$\text{moles of HCl added} = \frac{(20 \times 0.1)}{1000} = 0.002\,mol$$

new volume = 250 cm³

$$\text{concentration of new solution} = \frac{0.002}{250} \times 1000 = 0.008\,M$$

As it is a strong monobasic acid, $[H^+] = 0.008\,M$, so $pH = -\log(0.008) = 2.1$.

Worked example 2

10 cm³ of a 1.5 mol dm⁻³ solution of potassium hydroxide are diluted to 2 dm³ in a volumetric flask. Determine the pH of the resulting solution at 25°C if $pK_w = 14$ at 25°C.

$$\text{moles of KOH added} = \frac{10 \times 1.5}{1000} = 0.015\,mol$$

new volume = 2 dm³ (2000 cm³)

$$\text{concentration of new solution} = \frac{0.015}{2000} \times 1000 = 0.0075\,mol\,dm^{-3}$$

As 1 mol of KOH contains 1 mol of OH^-, $[OH^-] = 0.0075\,mol\,dm^{-3}$.

$$pOH = -\log[OH^-] \quad so \quad pOH = -\log(0.0075) = 2.12$$

$$pK_w = 14 = pH + pOH \quad so \quad pH = 14 - 2.12 = 11.88$$

Neutralisations

Worked example 3

Calculate the pH of the resulting solution when 25.0 cm³ of 0.2 M sodium hydroxide solution are added to 25.0 cm³ of 0.25 M hydrochloric acid.

This style of question is all about the number of moles of a reactant that are left over.

$$NaOH + HCl \rightarrow NaCl + H_2O$$

Examiner tip

You can also determine the dilution factor to determine the new concentration of acid or alkali. In the first example, the dilution factor is 12.5 (= total volume after dilution/initial volume added) as long as the units are the same for volume. The diluted solution is 12.5 times more dilute than the original solution:

$$\frac{0.1}{12.5} = 0.008\,M$$

The dilution factor in the second example is

$200\left(\frac{2000}{10}\right)$, so the diluted

solution of KOH is 200 times more dilute than the original solution:

$$\frac{1.5}{200} = 0.0075\,mol\,dm^{-3}$$

NaOH and HCl react in a 1:1 ratio.

$$\text{initial moles of NaOH} = \frac{25 \times 0.2}{1000} = 0.005\,\text{mol}$$

$$\text{initial moles of HCl} = \frac{25 \times 0.25}{1000} = 0.00625\,\text{mol}$$

$$NaOH + HCl \rightarrow NaCl + H_2O$$

0.005 mol of NaOH reacts with 0.005 mol of HCl, so:

0.00625 – 0.005 = 0.00125 mol of HCl remaining

new total volume of solution = 25 + 25 = 50 cm^3

$$\text{new concentration of reactant in excess} = \frac{\text{moles of reactant in excess}}{\text{volume of new solution (cm}^3)} \times 1000$$

$$\text{new concentration of reactant (HCl) in excess} = \frac{0.00125}{50} \times 1000 = 0.025\,\text{M}$$

As HCl is a strong monobasic acid, [H$^+$] = 0.025 M.

$$pH = -\log\,[H^+] = -\log(0.025) = 1.6$$

Worked example 4

Close to the end point of a titration 24.9 cm^3 of 0.5 mol dm^{-3} sulfuric acid have been added to 25.0 cm^3 of 1.0 mol dm^{-3} sodium hydroxide solution. If $K_w = 1.0 \times 10^{-14}$ mol^2 dm^{-6} at 25°C, determine the pH at this temperature.

$$\text{initial moles of } H_2SO_4 = \frac{24.9 \times 0.5}{1000} = 0.01245\,\text{mol}$$

$$\text{initial moles of NaOH} = \frac{25.0 \times 1.0}{1000} = 0.025\,\text{mol}$$

$$2NaOH + H_2SO_4 \rightarrow Na_2SO_4 + 2H_2O$$

From the equation, 2 mol of NaOH reacts with 1 mol of H$_2$SO$_4$. 0.01245 mol of H$_2$SO$_4$ reacts with 0.0249 mol of NaOH. NaOH is the reactant in excess.

moles of NaOH in excess = 0.025 – 0.0249 = 0.0001 mol

new total volume of solution = 25 + 24.9 = 49.9 cm^3

$$\text{new concentration of reactant in excess} = \frac{\text{moles of reactant in excess}}{\text{volume of new solution (cm}^3)} \times 1000$$

$$\text{new concentration of reactant (NaOH) in excess} = \frac{0.0001}{49.9} \times 1000 = 0.002\,\text{mol dm}^{-3}$$

As 1 mol of NaOH contains 1 mol of OH$^-$, [OH$^-$] = 0.002 mol dm^{-3}.

$$[H^+] = \frac{K_w}{[OH^-]} = \frac{1.0 \times 10^{-14}}{0.002} = 5 \times 10^{-12}\,\text{mol dm}^{-3}$$

$$pH = -\log[H^+] = -\log(5 \times 10^{-12}) = 11.3$$

Examiner tip
The pOH could have been determined and the pH determined from the pK$_w$, but either method is acceptable.

Buffers

A buffer is a solution formed from a weak acid and its salt. The buffering action is represented by the general equation:

$$HA \rightleftharpoons H^+ + A^-$$

where HA is the undissociated acid, A^- is the anion and H^+ are hydrogen ions.

Explanation of buffering action

When small quantities of acid or alkali are added, the buffer resists the change in pH that these would cause. You might be asked to explain how the buffer resists the change in pH.

Addition of dilute acid

- Extra hydrogen ions are added.
- The anion in the buffer reacts with H^+ ($A^- + H^+ \rightarrow HA$).
- The extra H^+ ions are removed.
- This maintains $[H^+]$ and maintains pH.

Addition of alkali

- Extra hydroxide, OH^-, ions are added.
- These react with undissociated acid in the buffer:

$$HA + OH^- \rightarrow A^- + H_2O$$

- The extra OH^- ions are removed.
- This maintains $[H^+]$ and maintains pH.

Calculating pH of a buffer

To determine the pH of a buffer you must determine the concentration of the anion $[A^-]$ — this usually equals the concentration of the salt — and the concentration of the weak acid $[HA]$ from the information given in the method used to prepare the buffer. The $[H^+]$ is determined from the K_a expression and pH is then calculated in the usual way. The main method of preparing a buffer is by adding a strong alkali such as sodium hydroxide solution to an excess of a weak acid in solution.

Addition of sodium hydroxide solution to an excess of the weak acid

In this buffer preparation the sodium hydroxide reacts with the weak acid to form the salt in situ. The weak acid must be in excess so no sodium hydroxide remains and the resulting solution contains the weak acid and its salt.

Worked example

$100\,cm^3$ of $0.05\,mol\,dm^{-3}$ nitrous acid (HNO_2) are mixed with $50\,cm^3$ of $0.04\,mol\,dm^{-3}$ sodium hydroxide solution. The K_a for nitrous acid is $7.2 \times 10^{-4}\,mol\,dm^{-3}$.

$$\text{moles of nitrous acid added } (HNO_2) = \frac{100 \times 0.05}{1000} = 0.005\,mol$$

$$\text{moles of sodium hydroxide added } (NaOH) = \frac{50 \times 0.04}{1000} = 0.002\,mol$$

The equation for the reaction between nitrous acid and sodium hydroxide solution is:

$$HNO_2 + NaOH \rightarrow NaNO_2 + H_2O$$

$0.002\,mol$ of NaOH will react with $0.002\,mol$ of HNO_2 (leaving $0.005 - 0.002 = 0.003\,mol$ of HNO_2) and forming $0.002\,mol$ of $NaNO_2$.

$$\text{moles of } HNO_2 \text{ after reaction} = 0.003\,mol$$

$$\text{moles of } NaNO_2 \text{ after reaction} = 0.002\,mol$$

$$\text{concentration of } HNO_2\,[HNO_2] = \frac{0.003}{150} \times 1000 = 0.02\,mol\,dm^{-3}$$

$$\text{concentration of } NaNO_2\,[NaNO_2] = [NO_2^-] = \frac{0.002}{150} \times 1000 = 0.0133\,mol\,dm^{-3}$$

$$K_a = \frac{[NO_2^-][H^+]}{[HNO_2]} = 7.2 \times 10^{-4}\,mol\,dm^{-3}$$

$$[H^+] = \frac{K_a \times [HNO_2]}{[NO_2^-]} = \frac{7.2 \times 10^{-4} \times 0.02}{0.0133} = 1.083 \times 10^{-3}\,M$$

$$pH = -\log[H^+] = -\log(1.083 \times 10^{-3}) = 2.97$$

Titration curves

A titration curve is a graph of pH against volume of alkali or acid added. A typical curve shows the initial pH of the acid or alkali and the point when neutralisation occurs. The shape of the curve shows the type of titration.

A vertical region in a (titration) curve is called an inflection point. An inflection point occurs at the equivalence point in the titration. The equivalence point is when the exact amount of the titrant (solute being added in solution from the burette) required for neutralisation has been added.

Analysis of titration curves

There are four different shapes of titration curve (Figure 18). The initial pH also gives a clue to the type of acid being titrated (or alkali if the curves go from higher pH to lower pH when acid is added to alkali). The volume (of acid or alkali) required for neutralisation (at the equivalence point) is also important but can be calculated when sketching a titration curve.

Examiner tip

Both solutions dilute each other and the sodium hydroxide reacts with some of the nitrous acid to form the salt, sodium nitrite ($NaNO_2$). The new total volume in this example is $150\,cm^3$ and this will be used to calculate the new concentrations of the weak acid and its salt.

Examiner tip

All of the sodium hydroxide has been used up leaving only some moles of the weak acid (HNO_2) and some moles of the salt ($NaNO_2$) in solution. The water formed is in the solution.

Examiner tip

In some cases the concentration of the weak acid and its salt may be the same. In this case $[H^+] = K_a$. The Henderson Hasselbalch equation can be used to calculate the pH of a buffer:

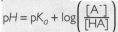

$$pH = pK_a + \log\left(\frac{[A^-]}{[HA]}\right)$$

where $[A^-]$ is the concentration of the anion and $[HA]$ is the concentration of the acid.

Knowledge check 13

What is a buffer?

Examiner tip

A titration curve can be plotted from pH readings taken during a titration. A known volume and concentration of acid or base solution in a conical flask is titrated with base or acid solution from a burette.

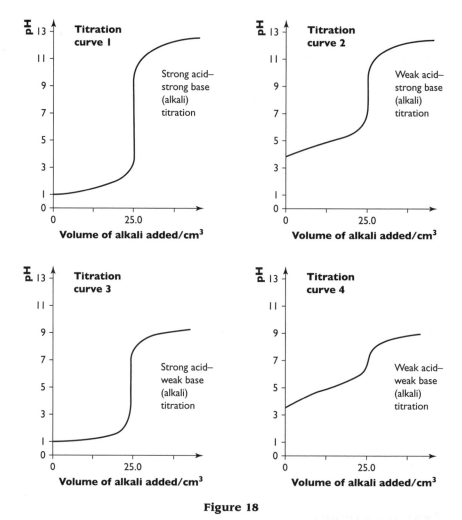

Figure 18

- For titration curve 1, the inflection point occurs between pH3 and pH10. This is indicative of a strong acid–strong base (alkali) titration. The initial pH of the acid is 1, which would suggest a strong acid.
- For titration curve 2, the inflection point occurs between pH6 and pH10. This is indicative of a weak acid–strong base (alkali) titration. The initial pH of the acid is almost 4, which would suggest a weak acid.
- For titration curve 3, the inflection point occurs between pH3 and pH8. This is indicative of a strong acid–weak base (alkali) titration. The initial pH of the acid is 1, which would suggest a strong acid.
- For titration curve 4, there is no major inflection point. This is indicative of a weak acid–weak base (alkali) titration. The initial pH of the acid is between 3 and 4, which would suggest a weak acid.

Sketching titration curves

If you are asked to sketch a titration curve you may be given:
- an initial calculation for the pH of the strong or weak acid — this is the starting pH for the curve where the volume of alkali added is equal to $0\,cm^3$
- the names of the acid and base (alkali) used — this will determine the shape of the titration curve, including the length of the point of inflection

CCEA A2 Chemistry

- the concentrations of the acid and base (alkali) used — the volume at which the point of inflection occurs can be calculated from the volume of base (alkali) required to neutralise the acid

Worked example

In a titration $0.2\,mol\,dm^{-3}$ sodium hydroxide solution is added to $25.0\,cm^3$ of $0.1\,mol\,dm^{-3}$ hydrochloric acid. Sketch the titration curve you would expect to obtain.

Initial pH:

HCl is a monobasic acid, so $[H^+] = 0.1\,mol\,dm^{-3}$.

$$\text{initial pH} = -\log(0.1) = 1$$

Shape:

Strong acid–strong base titration, so curve shaped like curve 1 — equivalence point with a change between 3 and 10 approximately.

Volume of base:

$$\text{number of moles of HCl present} = \frac{25 \times 0.1}{1000} = 0.0025$$

Equation:

$$NaOH + HCl \rightarrow NaCl + H_2O$$

1 mol of NaOH reacts with 1 mol of HCl.

0.0025 mol of HCl reacts with 0.0025 mol of NaOH.

$$\text{volume of NaOH} = \frac{0.0025 \times 1000}{0.2} = 12.5\,cm^3$$

The titration curve for this neutralisation looks like Figure 19.

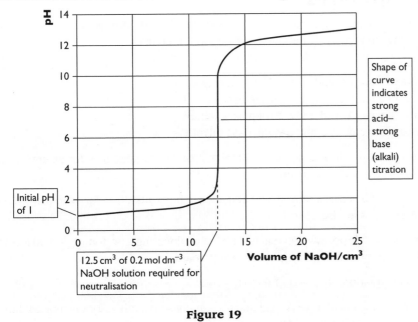

Figure 19

Examiner tip

The titration curve may be for a volume of acid added to a volume of alkali. Work out the initial pH of the strong alkali — this is the initial pH. The volume required for neutralisation is determined in the same way — the shape of curve is the same but reversed. This would be an unusual question but could be asked for a strong base (alkali) with an acid.

Table 9

Indicator	pH range of colour change
thymol blue	1.2–2.8
methyl orange	3.1–4.4
methyl red	4.4–6.2
bromothymol blue	6.0–7.6
phenolphthalein	8.3–10.0

Examiner tip

Methyl orange and phenolphthalein are the main indicators of choice. Both can be used for strong acid–strong base (alkali) titrations. Methyl orange is used for strong acid–weak base (alkali) titrations. Phenolphthalein is used for weak acid–strong base (alkali) titrations. A pH meter must be used for weak acid–weak base (alkali) titrations as there is no inflection point.

Knowledge check 14

State the colour of phenolphthalein in a solution of pH 12.

Examiner tip

If you are presented with solutions of two salts of different weak acids of equal concentration, for example 0.1 M solutions of sodium ethanoate (CH_3COONa) and 0.1 M sodium cyanide (NaCN), the more alkaline solution will be the salt of the acid with the lower K_a (or highest pK_a). K_a of ethanoic acid is $1.8 \times 10^{-5}\,mol\,dm^{-3}$; K_a for hydrocyanic acid is $6.3 \times 10^{-10}\,mol\,dm^{-3}$. The solution of sodium cyanide will have the higher pH (most alkaline).

Indicators for titrations

The choice of indicator for an acid–base (alkali) titration depends on the pH range in which the indicator changes colour. The colour change pH range of the indicator must be in the inflection point of the titration curve (the pH range of the equivalence point).

Table 9 shows some common indicators and the pH ranges of their colour change.

For a strong acid–strong base (alkali) titration the inflection point occurs between pH 3 and 10, so any of the indicators except thymol blue would work.

For a strong acid–weak base (alkali) titration, the inflection point occurs between pH 3 and 8, so any indicator in this range would work (i.e. methyl orange, methyl red and bromothymol blue).

For a weak acid–strong base (alkali) titration, the inflection point occurs between pH 6 and 10, so any indicator in this range would work (i.e. bromothymol blue or phenolphthalein).

Table 10 shows the colour changes of some common indicators used in titrations.

Table 10

Indicator	Colour change when adding acid to alkali	Colour change when adding alkali to acid
methyl orange	yellow to orange/red/pink	red/pink to orange/yellow
phenolphthalein	pink to colourless	colourless to pink

Salt hydrolysis

A salt is a compound formed when all or some of the H^+ ions in an acid are replaced by positive ions (usually metal ions or ammonium ions).

Salts can be:

- salts of a strong acid and a strong base (alkali)
- salts of a strong acid and a weak base (alkali)
- salts of a weak acid and a strong base (alkali)
- salts of a weak acid and a weak base (alkali)

A solution of a salt of a strong acid and a strong base (alkali) — for example, NaCl, K_2SO_4, $NaNO_3$, KCl — is **neutral**.

A solution of a salt of a strong acid and a weak base (alkali) — for example, NH_4NO_3, $(NH_4)_2SO_4$ — is **acidic**.

Explanation: The positive ion reacts with water, donating a proton (H^+ ion) to form the acidic hydronium ions. This gives an acidic solution.

Example equation: $NH_4^+ + H_2O \rightleftharpoons NH_3 + H_3O^+$

A solution of a salt of a weak acid and a strong base (alkali) — for example, solutions of CH_3COONa, HCOOK and NaCN — are **alkaline**.

Explanation: The negative ion reacts with water; the water donates a proton to the negative ions, leaving OH⁻ ions in solution. This gives an alkaline solution.

Example equation: $CN^- + H_2O \rightleftharpoons HCN + OH^-$

A solution of a salt of a weak acid and a weak base, for example CH_3COONH_4, is either acidic or alkaline depending on dissociation of the strong acid and the strong base (alkali). However, it will have a pH value below that of the same concentration of a salt of a weak acid and a strong base but above that of the same concentration of a salt of a strong acid and a weak base.

Summary

- An acid is a proton donor; a base is a proton acceptor; a proton is a hydrogen ion (H^+).
- $pH = -\log[H^+]$ where $[H^+]$ represents the concentration of H^+ in $mol\,dm^{-3}$ (M).
- The pH of a strong acid can be calculated from: $[H^+]$ = concentration of the acid × basicity of the acid $pH = -\log[H^+]$
- $K_w = [H^+][OH^-] = 1.0 \times 10^{-14}\,mol^2\,dm^{-6}$ at 25°C
- $pK_w = pH + pOH$

- A buffer is a solution that resists small changes in pH when small amounts of acid or alkali are added.
- The indicator in a titration depends on the pH range of the equivalence point in the titration.
- Salts of strong acids and strong bases are neutral in solution; salts of strong acids and weak bases are acidic in solution; salts of weak acids and strong bases are alkaline in solution.

Isomerism

Isomers that exhibit optical activity are called **optical isomers**.

Plane-polarised light is light that has been passed through a polarising filter. The waves of plane-polarised light all travel in the same plane so the plane can be rotated to the left or right. Optical isomers are often called stereoisomers and geometric isomers. Geometric isomers have the same structural formula but they differ in the three-dimensional arrangement of atoms in space. Optical isomers are non-superimposable.

Molecules with a **chiral centre** exhibit optical isomerism.

There are two types of optical isomers — **d** and **l**.
- **d** stands for **d**extrorotatory — this isomer rotates the plane of plane-polarised light to the right.
- **l** stands for **l**aevorotatory — this isomer rotates the plane of plane-polarised light to the left.

Drawing optical isomers

Based on the name or structure you are given, determine if the molecule has an asymmetric centre (or chiral centre). Draw this carbon as a tetrahedral carbon (Figure 20) and attach the four different groups to this carbon atom. The groups can be atoms (H, F, Cl, Br, I), simple groups such as OH, CH_3, CN, COOH, NH_2, or more complex groups such as $CH_2CH(OH)CH_2OH$ or CH_2CH_2CHO.

Optical isomers are molecules that exist as non-superimposable mirror images.

A **chiral centre** (or asymmetric centre) is a carbon atom with four different atoms or groups bonded to it.

> **Examiner tip**
> A molecule that does not have a chiral centre is described as optically inactive. Optically inactive substances **cannot** rotate the plane of plane-polarised light.

Optically active substances rotate the plane of plane-polarised light.

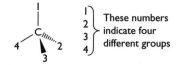

Figure 20

The optical isomers are shown by either reflecting the isomer in an imaginary mirror (Figure 21a) or simply exchanging any two of the groups attached to the chiral carbon atom (Figure 21b).

Figure 21

One of these two optical isomers would rotate the plane of plane-polarised light to the left and the other to the right.

Worked example 1

Lactic acid, $CH_3CH(OH)COOH$, is optically active. Identfy the asymmetric centre, label it with an asterisk (*) and draw the two optical isomers.

The central carbon atom has four different groups bonded to a single carbon atom (H, CH_3, OH and COOH).

$CH_3\overset{*}{C}H(OH)COOH$ — chiral centre (asymmetric centre) labelled with *

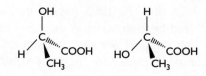

These two optical isomers are shown by simply exchanging two of the groups bonded to the asymmetric centre.

Worked example 2

How many chiral centres are present in the molecule shown?

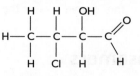

You need to look at the individual carbon atoms with four different groups bonded:

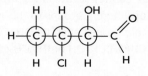

The three circled carbon atoms have four groups bonded to them. The CHO group has a carbon atom but it does not have four different groups bonded. The carbon atom on the left has three H atoms bonded to it so it cannot be a chiral centre because there are not four different groups bonded to this atom. This leaves the two other carbon atoms. Examining each individually:

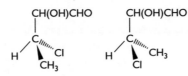

There are four different groups bonded to this carbon atom, so it is an asymmetric centre

These are the two isomers at this asymmetric centre:

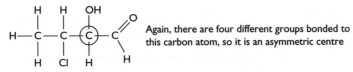

At the next carbon atom:

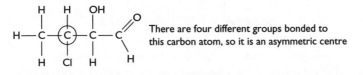

Again, there are four different groups bonded to this carbon atom, so it is an asymmetric centre

These are the two isomers at this asymmetric (chiral) centre:

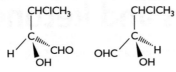

The molecule contains *two* chiral centres.

Functional group isomers

Functional group isomers are a class of structural isomers that have the same molecular formula but have a completely different structural formula, with a different functional group.

Worked example 1

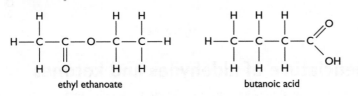

ethyl ethanoate   butanoic acid

These molecules have completely different structures yet have the same molecular formula ($C_4H_8O_2$). Ethyl ethanoate is an **ester** and butanoic acid is a **carboxylic acid**.

Examiner tip

In the A-level course there are two main examples of organic compounds that are functional group isomers of each other:

- **Esters** are functional group isomers of **carboxylic acids**.
- **Aldehydes** are functional group isomers of **ketones**.

Worked example 2

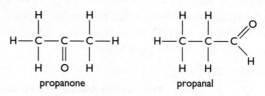

propanone   propanal

These molecules have completely different structures yet have the same molecular formula (C_3H_6O). Propanone is a **ketone** and propanal is an **aldehyde**.

Summary

- A chiral centre (or asymmetric centre) is a carbon atom with four different groups bonded to it.
- Optical isomers have a chiral centre and they exhibit optical isomerism.
- Optically active isomers are non-superimposable mirror images that have the ability to rotate the plane of plane-polarised light.
- Functional group isomers have the same molecular formula but a different functional group.
- Aldehydes are functional group isomers of ketones and carboxylic acids are functional group isomers of esters.

Aldehydes and ketones

The general formula for aldehydes and ketones is $C_nH_{2n}O$. They are functional group isomers (Figure 22).

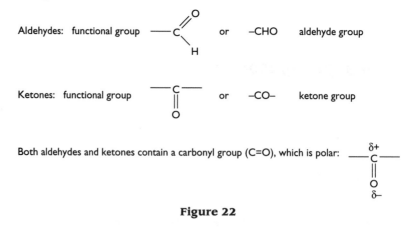

Figure 22

Nomenclature of aldehydes and ketones

The nomenclature of aldehydes ends in -al; ketones end in -one. The first members of the aldehyde and ketone homologous series are shown in Figure 23.

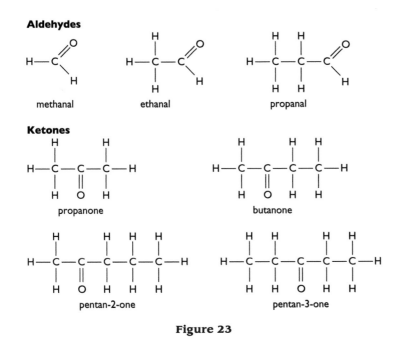

Figure 23

Physical properties of aldehydes and ketones

Short-chain aldehydes and ketones are **liquids**.

- The permanent dipole on the C=O bond causes attractions between molecules that require more energy to break them than for van der Waals forces alone.

Short-chain aldehydes and ketones are **miscible with water**.

- The permanent dipole on the C=O bond allows molecules to break hydrogen bonds between water molecules and form hydrogen bonds with water molecules.

Oxidation and reduction of aldehydes and ketones

Many of the chemical properties of aldehydes and ketones are based on the fact that aldehydes can undergo 'mild oxidation' but ketones cannot. Both aldehydes and ketones can be reduced. Mild oxidation maintains the carbon chain length.

Formation of aldehydes and ketones

Aldehydes are formed from the mild oxidation of primary (1°) alcohols. Prolonged oxidation of a primary alcohol forms a carboxylic acid. For example, using ethanol as the primary alcohol:

$$CH_3CH_2OH + [O] \rightarrow CH_3CHO + H_2O$$
ethanol ethanal

$$CH_3CHO + [O] \rightarrow CH_3COOH$$
ethanal ethanoic acid

Examiner tip

Ketones require a minimum of three carbon atoms, as there must be a C=O in the middle of the molecule. So propanone is the simplest ketone. Ketones with five or more carbon atoms require a number to indicate the position of the CO group. Aldehydes do not require a number for the position of the CHO group because it is at the end of the chain. Aldehydes have common names such as formaldehyde for methanal and acetaldehyde for ethanal. Propanone is often called acetone, and is the main solvent in nail varnish remover.

Examiner tip

Practically, prolonged oxidation would involve heating the mixture under reflux. Heating while distilling would yield the aldehyde because the aldehyde has a lower boiling point than the alcohol or the carboxylic acid.

The prolonged mild oxidation of a primary alcohol can be represented as:

$$CH_3CH_2OH + 2[O] \rightarrow CH_3COOH + H_2O$$
$$\text{ethanol} \qquad\qquad \text{ethanoic acid}$$

Ketones are formed from the mild oxidation of secondary (2°) alcohols. For example, using propan-2-ol as the secondary alcohol:

$$CH_3CH(OH)CH_3 + [O] \rightarrow CH_3COCH_3 + H_2O$$
$$\text{propan-2-ol} \qquad\qquad \text{propanone}$$

Common mild oxidising agents

The reactions of the common mild oxidising agents require mixing the aldehyde (or ketone) with the oxidising reagent and *warming* the mixture in a warm water bath. The aldehyde shows the expected change but with the ketone the solution will not change.

Acidified (potassium) dichromate solution

Acidified potassium dichromate solution (or acidified potassium dichromate(VI) solution) is a common oxidising agent used for mild oxidation in organic chemistry.

The equation for reduction of dichromate(VI) to chromium(III) is given below. The colour changes from orange to green. Dichromate(VI) ions give an **orange solution** and chromium(III) ions give a **green solution**:

$$Cr_2O_7^{2-} + 14H^+ + 6e^- \rightarrow 2Cr^{3+} + 7H_2O$$
$$\text{orange} \qquad\qquad\qquad \text{green}$$
$$\text{solution} \qquad\qquad\qquad \text{solution}$$

Tollens' reagent

Tollens' reagent (often incorrectly written as Tollen's reagent) is an ammoniacal solution of silver(I) nitrate.
- Tollens' reagent is a colourless solution.
- Tollens' reagent reacts with aldehydes but not with ketones.
- The silver(I) ions, Ag^+, are reduced to silver according to the equation:

$$Ag^+ + e^- \rightarrow Ag$$

- The solution changes from **colourless** to a **silver mirror** if the silver ions are reduced by the oxidation of an aldehyde. The solution remains colourless with a ketone.

Fehling's solution

Fehling's solution is a mixture of Fehling's solution 1 (copper(II) sulfate solution) and Fehling's solution 2 (mixture of sodium tartrate and sodium hydroxide solution). The resulting solution contains copper(II) ions complexed with tartrate ion.
- Fehling's solution is a **blue solution**.
- Fehling's solution reacts with aldehydes but not with ketones.
- The copper(II) ions are reduced to copper(I) oxide, Cu_2O, which appears as a **red precipitate**.

- The equation can be represented by:

$$Cu^{2+} + e^- \rightarrow Cu^+$$

where Cu^{2+} is blue in solution and the solid copper(I) oxide is a red precipitate.

Common reactions of aldehydes and ketones

Aldehydes and ketones undergo some common reactions because they contain the carbonyl (C=O) group. With hydrogen cyanide, aldehydes and ketones react to form cyanohydrins. With 2,4-dinitrophenylhydrazine, they react to form 2,4-dinitrophenylhydrazones.

Hydrogen cyanide (HCN)

Hydrogen cyanide is a toxic gas so any reaction with an aldehyde or ketone is carried out using a solution of sodium or potassium cyanide with sulfuric acid. This is not normally carried out in a school laboratory owing to the toxic nature of HCN. HCN is covalently bonded as H–C≡N.

General reaction:

aldehyde/ketone + HCN → cyanohydrin

For example, with an aldehyde (using ethanal):

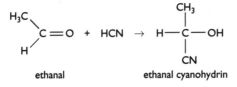

ethanal   ethanal cyanohydrin

For example, with a ketone (using propanone):

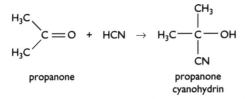

propanone   propanone
                           cyanohydrin

Mechanism of the reaction of hydrogen cyanide with an aldehyde or ketone

Aldehydes and ketones react with hydrogen cyanide by **nucleophilic addition**.

When drawing the mechanism for the reaction of hydrogen cyanide with an aldehyde or a ketone, it is best to draw the aldehyde or ketone as shown. The HCN molecule splits to give H^+ and cyanide ions, CN^-. The CN^- is the nucleophile:

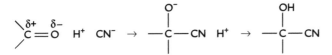

Examiner tip

The correct name for ethanal cyanohydrin is 2-hydroxypropanenitrile. The CN group has a higher priority than the OH group. The longest chain containing the CN is 3C long, so propanenitrile; the OH group is bonded to the second carbon counting from the C of the CN group.

Examiner tip

The correct name for propanone cyanohydrin is 2-hydroxy-2-methylpropanenitrile. The CN group has a higher priority than the OH group. The longest chain containing the CN is 3C long, so propanenitrile; the OH group and CH_3 group are bonded to the second carbon counting from the C of the CN group.

A **nucleophile** is an electron-rich molecule or negative ion that attacks an electron-deficient region and donates a pair of electrons. Nucleophiles have a lone pair of electrons.

An **addition reaction** is one in which a π (pi) bond of a double covalent bond is broken and species are added across the bond.

Knowledge check 16

Name the mechanism by which hydrogen cyanide reacts with ethanal.

2,4-dinitrophenylhydrazine

2,4-dinitrophenylhydrazine, $C_6H_3(NO_2)_2NHNH_2$, has the following structure:

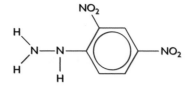

The structure is best remembered by building it up from hydrazine (H_2NNH_2). Remove a hydrogen from hydrazine and attach a benzene ring to give phenylhydrazine. Two nitro (NO_2) groups are added to the benzene ring in the 2 and 4 positions (Figure 24).

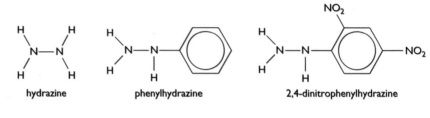

hydrazine   phenylhydrazine   2,4-dinitrophenylhydrazine

Figure 24

2,4-dinitrophenylhydrazine reacts with both aldehydes and ketones to form a 2,4-dinitrophenylhydrazone. For example with ethanal:

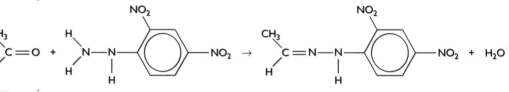

- The reaction is a condensation reaction (water is eliminated). The product is named using the name of the aldehyde or ketone followed by 2,4-dinitrophenylhydrazone, for example 'ethanal 2,4-dinitrophenylhydrazone'.

- 2,4-dinitrophenylhydrazine can be used as a method for identifying aldehydes and ketones — the 2,4-dinitrophenylhydrazone formed is a solid that can be purified and its melting point determined. Comparison of the melting point with a table of known values could identify the aldehyde or ketone.

- The 2,4-dinitrophenylhydrazone derivatives are all orange/yellow solids.

- The solution of 2,4-dinitrophenylhydrazine is often called Brady's reagent.

Preparation of a pure sample of a 2,4-dinitrophenylhydrazone derivative

- Mix the aldehyde or ketone with 2,4-dinitrophenylhydrazine solution.
- An orange/yellow precipitate forms (if a precipitate does not form, add some dilute sulfuric acid and warm the mixture).

- Suction-filter to obtain the solid.

Suction-filtration is faster and gives a drier product. The following points explain the process of **recrystallisation**.

- Dissolve the solid in a minimum volume of hot solvent (usually ethanol).

The solvent chosen for recrystallisation must be one in which the substance is soluble at high temperatures and much less soluble or insoluble at lower temperatures — this ensures that it will crystallise as it cools. A minimum volume of hot solvent is used to ensure that as much of the solute is obtained as possible.

- Filter the solution through fluted filter paper while hot to remove any insoluble impurities.
- Allow the solution to cool and crystallise.
- Suction-filter to obtain the solid crystals and wash with a little cold water.
- Dry the crystals between two sheets of filter paper.
- Determine the melting point of the solid to check purity.

A melting point is carried out by firstly sealing a capillary tube at one end (by heating in a blue Bunsen flame) and tapping some of the sample into it. The capillary tube is placed in a melting point apparatus and heated rapidly until about 10–15 degrees below the expected melting point, followed by slow heating. The temperature at which melting starts and ends is recorded. Pure solids have a sharp melting point. Impure solids melt over a range and at a lower temperature than expected. If the solid is impure you should carry out the recrystallisation again.

Reduction reactions

Both aldehydes and ketones can be reduced to alcohols. Aldehydes are reduced to primary alcohols and ketones to secondary alcohols. The reduction is carried out using lithal ($LiAlH_4$) dissolved in dry ether. The reaction is heated under reflux. The reducing agent can be represented as [H] in an equation:

$$CH_3CHO + 2[H] \rightarrow CH_3CH_2OH$$
$$\text{ethanal} \qquad\qquad \text{ethanol}$$

$$CH_3COCH_2CH_3 + 2[H] \rightarrow CH_3CH(OH)CH_2CH_3$$
$$\text{butanone} \qquad\qquad\qquad \text{butan-2-ol}$$

> **Examiner tip**
> Practically, the aldehyde or ketone is added to the solution of 2,4-dinitrophenylhydrazine as the solid derivative would dissolve in an excess of the aldehyde or ketone.

> **Examiner tip**
> The 2,4-dinitrophenyl-hydrazone derivatives are large molecules with a lot of electrons (large van der Waals forces between molecules) and they have polar NO_2 groups, which create large permanent dipole and van der Waals attractions between molecules. These require a lot of energy to break, so increasing the melting point.

> **Examiner tip**
> You should revise the practical points and the diagrams from the preparation of iodoform in AS 2 as you may be asked about these in A2 1 or A2 practical papers. The same techniques are used for the preparation of any organic solid.

Summary

- Aldehydes and ketones contain the carbonyl group (C=O); the general formula for both aldehydes and ketones is $C_nH_{2n}O$.
- Aldehydes and ketones both react with 2,4-dintrophenylhydrazine and hydrogen cyanide.
- The mechanism of the reaction of hydrogen cyanide is nucleophilic addition, with the cyanide ion, CN^-, acting as the nucleophile.

- Aldehydes undergo mild oxidation to carboxylic acids; ketones cannot undergo mild oxidation; this can be used to distinguish between aldehydes and ketones.
- Mild oxidising agents used to distinguish between aldehydes and ketones include acidified potassium dichromate solution, Fehling's solution and Tollens' reagent.
- Aldehydes and ketones can be identified using 2,4-dintrophenylhydrazine.

Carboxylic acids

The general formula for carboxylic acids is $C_nH_{2n}O_2$.

Functional group or –COOH (carboxyl group)

Naming carboxylic acids

Carboxylic acids are named using the ending -oic acid. No positional number is required for one COOH group but the carbon atom of this group is carbon 1 in the chain. Most carboxylic acids contain C–C single bonds and these are alkanoic acids. Carboxylic acids with C=C are alkenoic acids. Figure 25 shows some examples.

Examiner tip
Remember to number the chain from the COOH group. The same applies to aldehydes. No number is required for the position of one COOH or CHO group in a molecule. Methanoic acid is commonly called formic acid and ethanoic acid is called acetic acid.

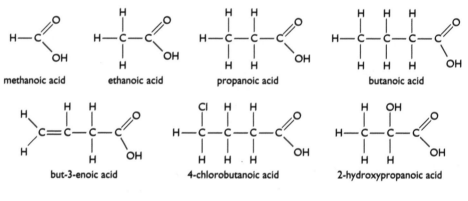

Figure 25

Properties of carboxylic acids

- Carboxylic acids have a sharp, irritating odour.
- Short-chain carboxylic acids are **liquids** — the polar OH group causes hydrogen bonds between molecules, which require a lot of energy to break them.
- Short-chain carboxylic acids are **miscible with water** — the polar OH group allows them to break hydrogen bonds between water molecules and form hydrogen bonds with water molecules.
- Carboxylic acids are **weak acids** — in aqueous solution they are only partially ionised.

Formation of carboxylic acids

Carboxylic acid can be formed by:
- mild oxidation of primary alcohols and aldehydes
- hydrolysis of esters
- hydrolysis of nitriles

Mild oxidation of primary alcohols and aldehydes

Carboxylic acids are produced when primary alcohols undergo prolonged mild oxidation. Primary alcohols are oxidised first to aldehydes and then the aldehydes are oxidised to carboxylic acids. For example, using [O] to represent the oxidising agent:

$$CH_3CH_2CH_2OH + 2[O] \rightarrow CH_3CH_2COOH + H_2O$$
propan-1-ol $\qquad\qquad$ propanoic acid

$$CH_3CH_2CHO + [O] \rightarrow CH_3CH_2COOH$$
propanal $\qquad\qquad$ propanoic acid

Hydrolysis of esters

Esters can be hydrolysed to form the carboxylic acid (or its salt) and the alcohol from which the ester was formed.

If **acid-catalysed hydrolysis** is used, the products are the carboxylic acid and the alcohol. The ester should be heated under reflux with dilute hydrochloric acid:

$$CH_3CH_2COOCH_3 + H_2O \rightarrow CH_3CH_2COOH + CH_3OH$$
methyl propanoate $\qquad$ propanoic acid $\quad$ methanol

If **alkaline-catalysed hydrolysis** is used, the salt of the carboxylic acid is formed with the alcohol. The ester should be heated under reflux with sodium hydroxide solution:

$$HCOOCH_2CH_3 + NaOH \rightarrow HCOONa + CH_3CH_2OH$$
ethyl methanoate $\qquad\qquad$ sodium methanoate $\quad$ ethanol

Hydrolysis of nitriles

Nitriles contain the $-C\equiv N$ functional group, which may be hydrolysed to form carboxylic acids. Nitriles may be hydrolysed using acid or alkali by heating under reflux.

- The first stage in the hydrolysis is the formation of the amide, which has the $-CONH_2$ functional group.
- The second stage is the formation of the acid with the removal of ammonia.
- If acid-catalysed hydrolysis is used, the carboxylic acid and the ammonium salt of the acid will be formed.
- If alkaline-catalysed hydrolysis is used, the salt of the carboxylic acid and ammonia will be formed.

Overall the hydrolysis occurs like this:

$$RCN + H_2O \rightarrow RCONH_2 + H_2O \rightarrow RCOOH + NH_3$$

Acid-catalysed hydrolysis produces the carboxylic acid and the ammonium salt of the dilute acid used, for example ammonium chloride if hydrochloric acid is used. For example:

$$CH_3CN + HCl + 2H_2O \rightarrow CH_3COOH + NH_4Cl$$
ethanenitrile $\qquad\qquad\qquad$ ethanoic acid

Alkaline-catalysed hydrolysis produces the salt of the carboxylic acid and ammonia. For example:

$$CH_3CN + NaOH + H_2O \rightarrow CH_3COONa + NH_3$$
ethanenitrile $\qquad\qquad\qquad$ sodium ethanoate

Examiner tip

The oxidising agent used is usually acidified potassium dichromate solution (acidified sodium dichromate solution can also be used). The reaction mixture is heated under reflux to form a solution of the carboxylic acid. The corresponding aldehyde could also undergo mild oxidation to the carboxylic acid. Reflux is heating a reaction mixture using a vertical condenser to return evaporated reactants and products to the reaction mixture by condensing them. You should revise the method of heating under reflux from AS 2.

Examiner tip

The carboxylic acid could be regenerated from the solution of its salt by adding a dilute mineral acid such as dilute hydrochloric acid. This is a common question.

Examiner tip

Acid-catalysed hydrolysis may be referred to as acid hydrolysis. This stems from reactions in which the acid is used up in a further reaction, as in the acid hydrolysis of nitriles. The acid is not seen to be a true catalyst as it is used up during the reaction.

Examiner tip

Alkaline catalysed hydrolysis (sometimes called base-catalysed hydrolysis) may be referred to as alkaline hydrolysis. Again, this stems from reactions in which the alkali is used up in a further reaction, as in the alkaline hydrolysis of esters and nitriles.

Reactions of carboxylic acids

The reactions of carboxylic acids can be divided into three categories:
- reactions of the OH group
- reactions as a weak acid
- reduction reactions

Reactions of the OH group

The main reactions of the OH group in carboxylic acids are with phosphorus pentachloride, PCl_5, thionyl chloride, $SOCl_2$, and in esterification reactions.

Phosphorus pentachloride, PCl_5

$$RCOOH \quad + \; PCl_5 \; \rightarrow \quad RCOCl \quad + POCl_3 + HCl$$
carboxylic acid   acid chloride

For example:

$$CH_3COOH \quad + \; PCl_5 \; \rightarrow \quad CH_3COCl \quad + POCl_3 + HCl$$
ethanoic acid   ethanoyl chloride

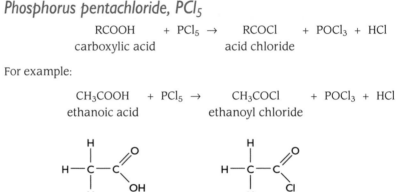

$POCl_3$ is called phosphorus oxychloride (or, properly, phosphorus(v) trichloride oxide). HCl is hydrogen chloride gas. During this reaction, there are misty fumes (of HCl) and the reaction is vigorous, with heat produced. The identity of HCl can be confirmed using a glass rod dipped in concentrated ammonia solution held in the gas. White smoke confirms the presence of HCl gas.

Thionyl chloride, $SOCl_2$

$$RCOOH \quad + \; SOCl_2 \; \rightarrow \quad RCOCl \quad + SO_2 + HCl$$
carboxylic acid   acid chloride

For example:

$$CH_3CH_2COOH \; + SOCl_2 \; \rightarrow \quad CH_3CH_2COCl \quad + SO_2 + HCl$$
propanoic acid   propanoyl chloride

SO_2 is sulfur dioxide gas. HCl is hydrogen chloride gas. During this reaction, there are misty fumes (of HCl) and the reaction is vigorous, with heat produced. Thionyl chloride is a corrosive liquid and it is not used in school laboratories.

Esterification

Esters were studied in AS2 and will be considered in more detail in the next section. Esters are condensation products of the reaction between a carboxylic acid and an alcohol. They contain the COO group — often called an ester link.

$$RCOOH \quad + \; R_1OH \; \rightarrow RCOOR_1 + H_2O$$
carboxylic acid   alcohol   ester

CCEA A2 Chemistry

where R and R_1 are alkyl groups — these may be the same or different. For example:

$$CH_3CH_2COOH \;+\; CH_3CH_2OH \;\rightarrow\; CH_3CH_2COOCH_2CH_3 \;+\; H_2O$$

propanoic acid   ethanol   ethyl propanoate

Reactions as a weak acid

Carboxylic acids react as typical weak acids. Some common reactions are described below.

With sodium carbonate

Sodium carbonate reacts with carboxylic acids, forming the sodium salt, carbon dioxide and water. The most obvious observation is the bubbles of gas produced. The solid sodium carbonate disappears. Bubbles of gas are observed when a solution of sodium carbonate is mixed with a carboxylic acid. For example:

$$2CH_3COOH \;+\; Na_2CO_3 \;\rightarrow\; 2CH_3COONa \;+\; CO_2 + H_2O$$

ethanoic acid   sodium carbonate   sodium ethanoate

With sodium hydroxide

Sodium hydroxide solution reacts with carboxylic acids, releasing heat. There are no other relevant observations as the solution remains colourless. For example:

$$CH_3CH_2COOH \;+\; NaOH \;\rightarrow\; CH_3CH_2COONa \;+\; H_2O$$

propanoic acid   sodium hydroxide   sodium propanoate

With ammonia

Ammonia solution reacts with carboxylic acids, forming a solution of the ammonium salt and releasing heat. Again there are no other relevant observations as the solution is colourless. For example:

$$CH_3COOH \;+\; NH_3 \;\rightarrow\; CH_3COONH_4$$

ethanoic acid   ammonia   ammonium ethanoate

More complex carboxylic acids

In many cases dibasic and tribasic weak acids are used in questions with **excess** of a reagent such as sodium carbonate or even other carbonates. Common examples are ethanedioic acid (commonly called oxalic acid) and 2-hydroxypropane-1,2,3-trioic acid (commonly called citric acid) — see Figure 26.

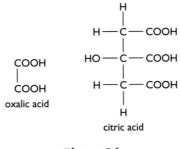

Figure 26

> **Examiner tip**
> This type of reaction is best monitored in a titration using an indicator, or in a thermometric titration where the temperature change is monitored. Neutralisation of weak acids using a strong alkali does not give out as much heat energy as a similar neutralisation of a strong acid. Some of the energy is used to dissociate the weak acid fully.

> **Examiner tip**
> Again this is best followed in a titration but there is no suitable indicator, so a pH meter is used. Ammonium compounds of weak acids are unstable and dehydrate when warmed to form amides. Amides are part of A22.

> **Examiner tip**
> Excess reagent means that all the COOH groups react. You should apply the same process, forming the salt from the anion (formed by removing all the H^+ from COOH groups — there is a negative charge on the anion for every H^+ removed) and use the charge to form the compounds with the metal ion.

Worked example

Write an equation for the reaction between excess magnesium carbonate and oxalic acid (ethanedioic acid).

The anion formed from ethanedioic acid is

$$\begin{array}{c} COO^- \\ | \\ COO^- \end{array}$$

The equation can be written as:

$$\begin{array}{c} COOH \\ | \\ COOH \end{array} + MgCO_3 \rightarrow \left(\begin{array}{c} COO \\ | \\ COO \end{array}\right)Mg + CO_2 + H_2O$$

Reduction reactions

Carboxylic acids are reduced to aldehydes and then further reduced to primary alcohols. The reduction is carried out by heating the carboxylic acid under reflux with lithal ($LiAlH_4$) in dry ether. The aldehyde can be distilled off if required but prolonged refluxing with lithal will produce the primary alcohol.

For example, using [H] to represent the reducing agent lithal:

$$CH_3COOH + 2[H] \rightarrow CH_3CHO + H_2O$$
$$\text{ethanoic acid} \qquad \text{ethanal}$$

$$CH_3CH_2COOH + 4[H] \rightarrow CH_3CH_2CH_2OH + H_2O$$
$$\text{propanoic acid} \qquad \text{propan-1-ol}$$

Preparation of a carboxylic acid from a primary alcohol

The example used is the preparation of ethanoic acid from ethanol:

- Add water and concentrated sulfuric acid to a pear-shaped flask.
- Swirl the solution and cool the flask.
- Add potassium dichromate (or sodium dichromate).
- Add anti-bump granules.
- Add the alcohol (ethanol) slowly with a vertical condenser in place and cool the reaction vessel in a water bath.
- Heat the mixture under reflux.
- Distil off the acid.

Summary

- Carboxylic acids contain the carboxyl (COOH) functional group and have the general formula $C_nH_{2n}O_2$.
- Carboxylic acid are weak acids, which react with metals, metal carbonates and metal hydroxides and ammonia.
- Carboxylic acids can be formed from the mild oxidation of primary alcohols and aldehydes or the hydrolysis of nitriles and esters.

- The OH group in carboxylic acids reacts with PCl_5 and $SOCl_2$ to form acid chlorides.
- Carboxylic acids react with alcohols to form esters. Acid chlorides also react with alcohols to form esters.
- Ethanoic acid can be prepared through the mild oxidation of ethanol by heating under reflux with acidified (sodium) dichromate solution.

Esters, fats and oils

Esters

Esters contain the functional group –COO–

$$-\overset{\underset{\displaystyle \|}{}}{C}-O-$$
$$\overset{}{O}$$

Esters are formed from the condensation reaction between an alcohol and a carboxylic acid. They can also be formed from the elimination reaction between an alcohol and an acid chloride (eliminating hydrogen chloride).

Esters are liquids with a characteristic fruity or solvent odour. They are immiscible with water as they are mostly non-polar.

Any reactions of esters are based around the polar ester link (–COO–). This ester link can be hydrolysed.

Nomenclature and structure

Esters are named based on the alcohol (converted to an alkyl name) and the acid (converted to the salt name). For example:
- ethanol and propanoic acid form ethyl propanoate
- methanol and ethanoic acid form methyl ethanoate

$$CH_3CH_2OH + CH_3CH_2COOH \rightleftharpoons CH_3CH_2COOCH_2CH_3 + H_2O$$
ethanol　　　propanoic acid　　　ethyl propanoate

Physical properties of esters

Esters are neutral liquids, which have a pleasant, fruity odour.

Solubility in water

Very small ester molecules are soluble in water but solubility decreases as the length of the chain increases. Table 11 gives the solubility of some esters. As the ester molecules become larger, the solubility in water decreases.

Table 11

Ester	Formula	RFM	Solubility (g per 100 g of water)
ethyl methanoate	$HCOOCH_2CH_3$	74	10.5
ethyl ethanoate	$CH_3COOCH_2CH_3$	88	8.7
ethyl propanoate	$CH_3CH_2COOCH_2CH_3$	102	1.7

The polar carbonyl group on the ester can form hydrogen bonds with water, but as the non-polar hydrocarbon chain increases in size, the ester molecule can no longer form hydrogen bonds effectively.

Examiner tip

The structure of an ester is based on the alcohol (minus its H from the OH) and the acid (minus its OH from the COOH) — this generates water as the condensation product. The ester link may be written as OOC if starting from the alcohol end or COO if starting from the acid end. Remember that the C of the COO came from the acid.

Knowledge check 18

Name the ester $CH_3CH_2COOCH_3$.

Boiling points

Esters are functional group isomers with carboxylic acids. Ethyl ethanoate ($CH_3COOCH_2CH_3$) has the same molecular formula as butanoic acid ($CH_3CH_2CH_2COOH$). The boiling points of these molecules are given in Table 12.

Table 12

Ester	Formula	Boiling point (°C)
ethyl ethanoate	$CH_3COOCH_2CH_3$	77.1
butanoic acid	$CH_3CH_2CH_2COOH$	164

The much higher boiling point of butanoic acid is due to hydrogen bonding between molecules of butanoic acid. The intermolecular bonding in ethyl ethanoate is mostly van der Waals forces of attraction and some permanent dipole attraction between the polar C=O groups.

As the length of the ester chain increases, so too does the boiling point (Table 13). The increase in the boiling point is caused by the increasing number of electrons, which causes more induced dipoles and hence greater van der Waals forces of attraction between the molecules. This increases the energy required to break the bonds between the molecules.

Table 13

Ester	Formula	RFM	Boiling point (°C)
methyl methanoate	$HCOOCH_3$	60	32
ethyl methanoate	$HCOOCH_2CH_3$	74	53
ethyl ethanoate	$CH_3COOCH_2CH_3$	88	77
ethyl propanoate	$CH_3CH_2COOCH_2CH_3$	102	98

Formation of esters

Esters can be formed in one of two ways:

- from an alcohol and a carboxylic acid
- from an alcohol and an acid chloride

Formation of an ester from an alcohol and a carboxylic acid

The OH of the carboxylic acid and the H of the OH group in the alcohol react to form water. For example:

$$CH_3CH_2OH \; + \; CH_3COOH \; \rightleftharpoons \; CH_3CH_2OOCCH_3 \; + \; H_2O$$
$$\text{ethanol} \qquad \text{ethanoic acid} \qquad \text{ethyl ethanoate}$$

Concentrated sulfuric acid is added to remove the water and promote the formation of the ester — the mixture is heated under reflux.

Formation of an ester from an alcohol and an acid chloride

The Cl of the acid chloride reacts with the H from the OH group in the alcohol to form HCl:

Examiner tip

Acid chlorides are formed from carboxylic acids using PCl_5 or $SOCl_2$. The use of equimolar amounts of the acid chloride and the alcohol produces a much higher yield of a much purer ester. Often the reaction with the alcohol and the carboxylic acid is written with a reversible arrow ($\rightleftharpoons$) and the reaction using the acid chloride is written using a conventional arrow ($\rightarrow$).

$$CH_3CH_2OH + \quad CH_3CH_2COCl \quad \rightarrow \quad CH_3CH_2OOCCH_2CH_3 + HCl$$

ethanol   propanoyl chloride   ethyl propanoate

The reaction of the acid chloride with the alcohol produces a higher yield of the ester (without the concentrated sulfuric acid or heating under reflux) because the gaseous product (HCl) is removed from the equilibrium mixture, which promotes the formation of the ester.

Reactions of esters

Esters can be hydrolysed using acid-catalysed hydrolysis or alkaline-catalysed hydrolysis. The products are different in each type of hydrolysis.

Esters can be hydrolysed to form the carboxylic acid (or its salt) and the alcohol from which the ester was formed.

If **acid-catalysed hydrolysis** is used, the products are the carboxylic acid and the alcohol. The ester should be heated under reflux with dilute hydrochloric acid:

$$CH_3COOCH_3 \quad + H_2O \rightarrow \quad CH_3COOH \quad + \quad CH_3OH$$

methyl ethanoate   ethanoic acid   methanol

If **alkaline-catalysed hydrolysis** is used, the salt of the carboxylic acid is formed with the alcohol. The ester should be heated under reflux with sodium hydroxide solution:

$$HCOOCH_2CH_3 \quad + NaOH \rightarrow \quad HCOONa \quad + CH_3CH_2OH$$

ethyl methanoate   sodium methanoate   ethanol

The alkaline hydrolysis of esters occurs in two steps:

$$HCOOCH_2CH_3 + H_2O \rightarrow HCOOH + CH_3CH_2OH$$

The carboxylic acid formed reacts with the alkali to form the salt:

$$HCOOH \quad + NaOH \rightarrow \quad HCOONa \quad + H_2O$$

methanoic acid   sodium methanoate

Many reactions of esters represented involve diesters or triesters, which have two or three ester linkages. Compounds like ethane-1,2-diol can have two OH groups so can form two ester links with two carboxylic acid molecules. Apply the same logic to the formation of these esters.

Preparation of an ester — ethyl ethanoate

- Place a mixture of the alcohol (ethanol) and concentrated sulfuric acid in a pear-shaped flask.
- Add a mixture of the alcohol (ethanol) and the carboxylic acid (ethanoic acid) slowly from a dropping funnel.
- Swirl the mixture.
- Add anti-bumping granules and assemble the apparatus for distillation.
- Heat the mixture gently and collect the distillate.
- Wash with sodium carbonate solution to remove acidic impurities.
- Add anhydrous calcium chloride to remove water.

Examiner tip
The reaction for acid-catalysed hydrolysis is written as the reaction with water and the acid acts as a catalyst. Sometimes the H^+ ions are written above the arrow.

Examiner tip
This is the hydrolysis catalysed by the alkali. Again the OH^- can be written above the arrow.

Examiner tip
The carboxylic acid could be regenerated from the solution of its salt by adding a dilute mineral acid such as dilute hydrochloric acid. This is a common question. Hydrolysis is a chemical reaction with water, where the water breaks bonds in the molecule.

- Filter or decant to remove the calcium chloride.
- Redistil and collect at the required temperature.

Examiner tip
For this preparation you should revise heating under reflux, distillation and the use of a separating funnel from AS 2. Sodium carbonate solution removes acidic impurities in the distillate. The ester is less dense than water so it is the upper layer. You can check which is the organic/aqueous layer by adding water; the aqueous layer will increase in volume. Anhydrous calcium chloride is the drying agent used to remove water impurities in the ester.

Fats

Fats are triesters of **propane-1,2,3-triol** (glycerol) and fatty acids. Glycerol has the structure:

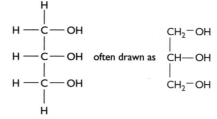

Examiner tip
You will need to remember that the systematic name for glycerol is propane-1,2,3-triol.

Fatty acids

Fatty acids are carboxylic acids with long hydrocarbon chains. The main fatty acids studied are stearic acid and oleic acid. The formula for stearic acid is written as $CH_3(CH_2)_{16}COOH$ or $C_{17}H_{35}COOH$. It is saturated, as the hydrocarbon chain contains no C=C double bonds. The formula for oleic acid is written as $CH_3(CH_2)_7CH=CH(CH_2)_7COOH$ or $C_{17}H_{33}COOH$. It is unsaturated as it contains a C=C double bond.

Formation of fats

1 mol of glycerol can react with 3 mol of fatty acid (Figure 27).

Examiner tip
Unsaturated fats contains fatty acids with C=C bonds. Saturated fats contain fatty acids containing only C−C bonds and no C=C bonds. You can spot a saturated fatty acid — the group attached to the COOH will have the composition $C_nH_{(2n+1)}$. If there are fewer than this number of hydrogen atoms, the fatty acid is unsaturated.

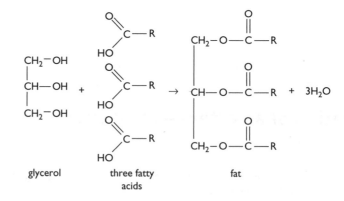

glycerol + three fatty acids → fat + $3H_2O$

Figure 27

Examiner tip
Fats are also called lipids or triglycerides. A fat formed from glycerol and three stearic acid molecules is called glyceryl tristearate or tristearin. A fat formed from glycerol and three oleic acid molecules is called glyceryl trioleate or triolein. A solid lipid is called a fat and a liquid lipid is called an oil. Some lipids contain one or two fatty acid chains. Triglycerides contain three fatty acid chains.

Formation of glyceryl tristearate

Figure 28 shows the formation of glyceryl tristearate from glycerol and stearic acid.

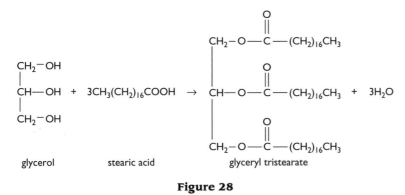

Figure 28

Examiner tip
You can apply this equation to the formation of any fat from glycerol and fatty acids. The three fatty acids in one fat molecule do not have to be the same. In natural fats there will be a mixture of many different fat molecules containing many different fatty acids.

Saturated and unsaturated fats

A fat that contains a large proportion of unsaturated fatty acids will likely be an oil rather than a solid fat. The more C=C bonds in the fatty acid chains, the fewer van der Waals forces of attraction there are between the fat molecules. More C=C bonds lead to the fat having a lower melting point and so the more likely it is that the fat is a liquid (an oil). This compares with a fat, which contains mostly saturated fatty acids. These will have greater van der Waals forces of attraction between the fat molecules, leading to a higher melting point. These fats are more likely to be solid. Fats with two or more C=C are called polyunsaturated.

Saturated and unsaturated fats in the diet

It is important to have a healthy balance of saturated and unsaturated fats in the diet. Saturated fats provide energy and insulation for the human body. They also increase levels of low-density lipoprotein (LDL) and can lead to coronary heart disease.

Unsaturated fats increase levels of high-density lipoprotein (HDL), which reduces the risk of coronary heart disease. They are also precursor molecules for prostaglandins. Artificial trans-unsaturated fats (added to processed food) increase the risk of coronary heart disease.

Reactions of fats and oils

The two main reactions of fats are hydrogenation of unsaturated fats and hydrolysis of fats.

Hydrogenation

Unsaturated fats react with hydrogen in the presence of finely divided nickel at 180°C. (Liquid) oils become (solid) fats due to the increase in van der Waals forces. Each C=C in the fatty acid chain reacts with H_2. 1 mol of the fat will react with x mol of H_2, where x is the number of C=C bonds in the fatty acid molecules to achieve total saturation (Figure 29).

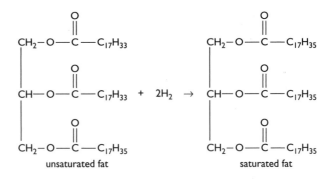

unsaturated fat   saturated fat

Figure 29

Hydrolysis of fats

Fats can be hydrolysed by acid-catalysed hydrolysis or alkaline-catalysed hydrolysis. Alkaline-catalysed hydrolysis of fats is the most commonly used and is called saponification. Saponification produces glycerol and the sodium (or potassium) salt of the fatty acid. The salt of the fatty acid is a soap — hence saponification (Figure 30).

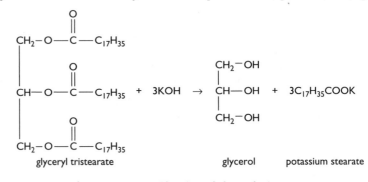

glyceryl tristearate   glycerol   potassium stearate

Figure 30 Saponification of glyceryl tristearate

Saponification value

The saponification value of a fat is the mass of potassium hydroxide in milligrams required to completely hydrolyse 1 gram of a fat or oil.

The higher the saponification value, the lower the RMM of the fat or oil. The lower the saponification value, the higher the RMM of the fat or oil.

Calculating saponification value from first principles

Figure 31 shows the fat glyceryl trioleate. 1 mol of glyceryl trioleate will react with 3 mol of KOH to hydrolyse the three ester bonds per molecule. The RMM of the molecule is 884.

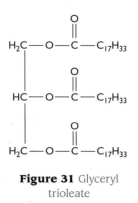

Figure 31 Glyceryl trioleate

1 g of the molecule is 1.131×10^{-3} mol, which will react with 3.393×10^{-3} mol of KOH.

1 g of the fat will react with $3.393 \times 10^{-3} \times 56$ (RMM of KOH) = 0.190 g of KOH, which is 190 mg of KOH per 1 g of the fat, so the saponification value of the fat is 190.

Calculating saponification value by titration

A known excess of alkali (KOH or NaOH) is added to the fat and refluxed. The solution is then titrated with standard hydrochloric acid to determine the potassium hydroxide (or sodium hydroxide) left over.

CCEA A2 Chemistry

Worked example

0.8g of a fat was mixed with 25.0 cm³ of 1.0 M potassium hydroxide solution in ethanol and boiled for 40 minutes.

25.0 cm³ of the resulting mixture was placed in a 250 cm³ volumetric flask and the volume made up to 250 cm³. 25.0 cm³ of this solution required 22.14 cm³ of 0.1 M hydrochloric acid for complete neutralisation.

Calculate the saponification value of the fat.

$$\text{moles of HCL used} = \frac{22.14 \times 0.1}{1000} = 0.002214 \, \text{mol}$$

$$KOH + HCl \rightarrow KCl + H_2O$$

moles of KOH remaining in diluted 25 cm³ = 0.002214 mol

moles of KOH in original 25 cm³ = 0.02214 mol

$$\text{original moles of KOH added} = \frac{25 \times 1}{1000} = 0.025$$

moles of KOH used in saponification of fat = 0.025 – 0.02214 = 0.00286 mol

mass of KOH used in saponification of fat = 0.00286 × 56 = 0.160 g

mass of KOH = 160 mg (mass of KOH used to saponify 0.8g of the fat)

$$\text{saponification value} = \frac{160}{0.8} = 200$$

Reaction with halogens/iodine/iodine monochloride

Unsaturated fats will react with halogens (most notably iodine, I_2) or iodine monochloride (ICl) at each C=C double bond. The amount of the halogen or ICl that reacts with a fat is a measure of the number of C=C double bonds (i.e. degree of unsaturation).

Iodine value

Practical method of determining iodine value

- Weigh the oil (mass of sample in grams = m).
- Dissolve it in a suitable saturated solvent such as 1,1,1-trichloroethane.
- Add Wijs solution (ICl solution).
- Leave this to stand in the dark for 30 minutes.
- Add excess KI solution (and water).
- Titrate liberated iodine with *standard* sodium thiosulfate solution (0.1 mol dm⁻³).
- Add starch indicator near the end point (when straw-coloured).
- The end point is reached when the solution changes from blue-black to colourless (V_1).
- Repeat using a blank with no oil (V_2).
- Calculate the iodine value using:

$$\text{iodine value} = \frac{(V_2 - V_1) \times 1.269}{m}$$

Examiner tip
A fat could be shown to be unsaturated by dissolving it in a suitable saturated solvent such as 1,1,1-trichloroethane and mixing it with bromine water. The yellow/orange/brown colour of the bromine water will change to colourless if the fat is unsaturated but will remain yellow/orange/brown if the fat is saturated.

The **iodine value** is the mass of iodine in grams required to react with 100g of the fat or oil.

Table 14

Fat/oil	Iodine value
Butter	30
Lard	60
Olive oil	80
Sunflower oil	120

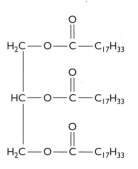

Figure 32

Understanding iodine values

The *higher* the iodine value, the *more unsaturated* the fat. The higher the iodine value, the more likely that the lipid is a (liquid) oil.

The *lower* the iodine value, the *more saturated* the lipid. The lower the iodine value, the more likely that the lipid is a (solid) fat.

Examples of typical iodine values are given in Table 14.

Calculating iodine value from first principles

Figure 32 shows the fat glyceryl trioleate. There is a C=C bond in each fatty acid chain ($C_{17}H_{33}$); if it was saturated, the alkyl chain would be $C_{17}H_{35}$ (C_nH_{2n+1}).

1 mol of this molecule will react with 3 mol of I_2.

The RMM of the molecule is 884.

100 g of the molecule is 0.1131 mol. This will react with 0.3393 mol of I_2.

This means that 100 g of the fat will react with 0.3393×254 (RMM of I_2) = 86.2 g of I_2. So the iodine value is 86.2.

Using saponification value and iodine value

A natural fat will contain a mixture of fatty acids. You can determine the average RMM of the fats and the average number of C=C bonds per fat molecule from the iodine value.

Worked example

An oil has a saponification value of 187.2 and an iodine value of 84.2. Calculate the average RMM of the fat molecules in the oil and from here the average number of C=C bonds per molecule of fat.

saponification value = 187.2 mg of KOH required to react with 1 g of the oil

$$0.1872 \text{ g of KOH} = \frac{0.1872}{56} = 3.343 \times 10^{-3} \text{ mol of KOH}$$

$$\text{number of moles of fat} = \frac{\text{moles of KOH}}{3} = \frac{3.343 \times 10^{-3}}{3} = 1.114 \times 10^{-3}$$

$$\text{average RMM of fat} = \frac{\text{mass of fat}}{\text{moles of fat}} = \frac{1}{1.114 \times 10^{-3}} = 897.67$$

iodine value = 84.2 g of I_2 required to react with 100 g of the oil.

$$84.2 \text{ g of } I_2 = \frac{84.2}{254} = 0.3315 \text{ mol of } I_2$$

$$100 \text{ g of the oil} = \frac{100}{897.67} = 0.1114 \text{ mol of fat (using average RMM)}$$

$$\text{mole ratio of the fat} : I_2 = 0.1114 : 0.3314 = 1 : \frac{0.3314}{0.1114} = 1 : 2.97$$

There are an average of 2.97 C=C bonds per fat molecule in the oil.

- Esters contain the COO group and have the general formula $C_nH_{2n}O_2$. They are functional group isomers of carboxylic acids.
- Esters are named according to the name of the alcohol and the carboxylic acid (or acid chloride) from which they are formed.
- Esters can undergo acid-catalysed hydrolysis or alkaline-catalysed hydrolysis.
- Fats are triesters of glycerol (propane-1,2,3-triol) and fatty acids.
- Fatty acids are long aliphatic (straight-chain) carboxylic acids.

- Liquid fats are called oils.
- Fats undergo alkaline-catalysed hydrolysis, which is called saponification.
- The saponification value of a fat is the mass of KOH in milligrams that is required to completely hydrolyse 1 g of the fat or oil.
- The iodine value of a fat is the mass of iodine in g that is required to react with 100 g of the fat or oil.
- A higher iodine value means a higher degree of unsaturation in the fat; the more unsaturated the fat, the lower the melting and boiling point.

Periodic trends

In this section you will examine the properties of the oxides and chlorides of the elements in period 3 (sodium to chlorine).

Reactions with oxygen and nature of the oxides

Sodium burns in air with a yellow/orange flame, producing a white solid, sodium oxide. Heat is released:

$$4Na + O_2 \rightarrow 2Na_2O$$

Sodium oxide is an ionic, basic oxide that reacts with water to produce a colourless solution of sodium hydroxide:

$$Na_2O + H_2O \rightarrow 2NaOH$$

Magnesium burns in air, producing a bright white light, releasing heat and producing a white solid, magnesium oxide:

$$2Mg + O_2 \rightarrow 2MgO$$

Magnesium oxide is an ionic, basic oxide. 10% of the solid formed on igniting magnesium is magnesium nitride, Mg_3N_2. Magnesium oxide is virtually insoluble in water but some does react to form magnesium hydroxide:

$$MgO + H_2O \rightarrow Mg(OH)_2$$

Aluminium powder burns in air with a white light, producing a white solid, aluminium oxide:

$$4Al + 3O_2 \rightarrow 2Al_2O_3$$

Aluminium oxide does not react with water. Aluminium oxide is an ionic, amphoteric oxide. Amphoteric oxides react with both acids and bases (alkalis).

With acid:

$$Al_2O_3 + 6H^+ \rightarrow 2Al^{3+} + 3H_2O$$

Examiner tip
Remember that when two colours are given separated by a solidus (/), only one of these colours should be given in an answer to a question, but be aware of both colours as the other may be referred to in a question..

Examiner tip

The aluminate ion can be written in various ways: $Al(OH)_4^-$, AlO_2^- or $Al(OH)_6^{3-}$. You should be able to recognise all of these as the aluminate ion.

With alkali:

$$Al_2O_3 + 2OH^- + 3H_2O \rightarrow 2Al(OH)_4^-$$

When aluminium oxide reacts with alkali, the aluminate ion, $Al(OH)_4^-$, is formed.

Silicon will burn in air if heated strongly enough to form silicon dioxide:

$$Si + O_2 \rightarrow SiO_2$$

Silicon dioxide does not react with water as the water cannot break up the giant covalent structure. Silicon dioxide is an acidic oxide that will react with alkalis:

$$SiO_2 + 2OH^- \rightarrow SiO_3^{2-} + H_2O$$

SiO_3^{2-} is the silicate ion.

Examiner tip

P_4O_{10} is the molecular formula of phosphorus(v) oxide; its empirical formula, P_2O_5, is sometimes used, but the structure of a molecule of P_4O_{10} contains four P atoms and ten O atoms.

Phosphorus ignites spontaneously in air, burning with a white flame and producing a white solid, P_4O_{10} (phosphorus(v) oxide):

$$P_4 + 5O_2 \rightarrow P_4O_{10}$$

Some phosphorus(III) oxide, P_4O_6, may be produced if the supply of oxygen is limited.

P_4O_{10} reacts with water, producing phosphoric(v) acid, H_3PO_4:

$$P_4O_{10} + 6H_2O \rightarrow 4H_3PO_4$$

P_4O_{10} is a covalent, acidic oxide.

Examiner tip

Check the oxidation number carefully, particularly for salts and acids of p-block elements: sulfate(vi) is sulfate (SO_4^{2-}), whereas sulfate(iv) is sulfite (SO_3^{2-}). Sulfuric(vi) acid is H_2SO_4, whereas sulfuric(iv) acid is H_2SO_3. The maximum oxidation number of a p-block element is + group number; the minimum oxidation number is the group number − 8. Sulfur has a maximum oxidation number of +6 and a minimum of −2.

Sulfur burns with a blue flame when heated in air (bluer flame in pure oxygen), releases heat and produces misty fumes of a pungent gas, sulfur dioxide, SO_2:

$$S + O_2 \rightarrow SO_2$$

Sulfur dioxide reacts with water, producing sulfurous acid, H_2SO_3.

$$SO_2 + H_2O \rightarrow H_2SO_3$$

Sulfur dioxide can be converted catalytically to sulfur trioxide, SO_3. Sulfur trioxide, SO_3, reacts very vigorously with water, producing sulfuric acid, H_2SO_4. SO_2 and SO_3 are covalent, acidic oxides.

Chlorine does not combine directly with oxygen, but the anhydride of perchloric acid, $HClO_4$, is Cl_2O_7 (dichlorine heptoxide). The Cl_2O_7 can be generated by adding P_4O_{10} to concentrated perchloric acid. Cl_2O_7 reacts with water to form perchloric acid.

$$Cl_2O_7 + H_2O \rightarrow 2HClO_4$$

Cl_2O_7 is a covalent, acidic oxide. Perchloric acid is also called chloric(vii) acid.

Reactions with chlorine and nature of the chlorides

Knowledge check 21

Name one oxide of a period 3 element that reacts with water, forming a strongly alkaline solution.

Sodium burns in chlorine with an orange flame, producing the white solid sodium chloride, NaCl:

$$2Na + Cl_2 \rightarrow 2NaCl$$

Sodium chloride is ionic. Sodium chloride dissolves in water to produce a colourless, neutral solution.

Magnesium burns in chlorine with a bright white light, producing the white solid magnesium chloride, $MgCl_2$:

$$Mg + Cl_2 \rightarrow MgCl_2$$

Magnesium chloride is ionic. It dissolves in water, producing a weakly acidic solution (around pH = 6) — the Mg^{2+} ion has a high charge density and water molecules surrounding it are more polarised and lose H^+ ions (proton abstraction).

Aluminium burns in chlorine to produce a yellow solid, aluminium chloride:

$$2Al + 3Cl_2 \rightarrow Al_2Cl_6$$

Aluminium chloride exists as the dimer Al_2Cl_6. It is covalent. The dimer occurs because a lone pair of electrons on the chlorine atom can donate to form a coordinate bond to the empty orbital on the aluminium atom of another $AlCl_3$. Al_2Cl_6 contains covalent and coordinate bonds. A dot-and-cross diagram is shown in Figure 33 with a simple bonding diagram.

Knowledge check 22

Name one chloride of a period 3 element that produces a neutral solution when dissolved in water.

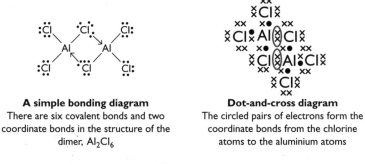

A simple bonding diagram
There are six covalent bonds and two coordinate bonds in the structure of the dimer, Al_2Cl_6

Dot-and-cross diagram
The circled pairs of electrons form the coordinate bonds from the chlorine atoms to the aluminium atoms

Figure 33

Aluminium chloride is hydrolysed by water, producing a strongly acidic solution:

$$Al_2Cl_6 + 6H_2O \rightarrow 2Al(OH)_3 + 6HCl$$

Phosphorus forms two chlorides, phosphorus(III) chloride, PCl_3 (also called phosphorus trichloride) and phosphorus(v) chloride, PCl_5 (also called phosphorus pentachloride).

Phosphorus(v) chloride is a pale yellow solid produced when phosphorus reacts with an excess of chlorine. The reaction is spontaneous and produces heat:

$$P_4 + 10Cl_2 \rightarrow 4PCl_5$$

Solid PCl_5 exists as molecular ions: PCl_4^+ and PCl_6^-. The bonding in *solid* PCl_5 is both covalent and ionic. PCl_5 reacts with excess water to form phosphoric(v) acid, H_3PO_4, and hydrogen chloride. The resulting solution is strongly acidic:

$$PCl_5(s) + 4H_2O(l) \rightarrow H_3PO_4(aq) + 5HCl(g)$$

This happens via a two stage reaction:

$$PCl_5 + H_2O \rightarrow POCl_3 + 2HCl$$

$$POCl_3 + 3H_2O \rightarrow H_3PO_4 + 3HCl$$

Summary

- Oxides of metals (Na, Mg and Al) are either basic (react with acids, forming salts, and may react with water, forming alkaline solutions) or amphoteric (react with both acids and alkalis).
- Oxides of non-metals can be neutral, but most are acidic (react with bases and may react with water, forming acidic solutions).
- Chlorides of Group I elements are neutral in solution because they do not undergo hydrolysis.
- Chlorides of Group II elements are slightly acidic (around pH = 6) in solution because they undergo partial hydrolysis.
- Aluminium chloride, Al_2Cl_6, exists as a dimer containing covalent and coordinate bonds; it is hydrolysed by water producing a strongly acidic solution.
- Phosphorus(v) chloride is also called phosphorus pentachloride. It reacts with water to produce a strongly acidic solution.

Environmental chemistry

Air pollution

The greenhouse effect is the heating of the surface of the planet due to the presence of an atmosphere that absorbs and emits **infrared radiation**.

The gases that absorb the infrared radiation (due to molecular vibrations — bending and stretching of the covalent bonds) in the atmosphere are called greenhouse gases. The ability of these gases to absorb the radiation and their concentration in the atmosphere are the two main factors that influence the greenhouse effect.

The solar radiation passes through the gases and is absorbed by the surface of the Earth. The surface emits the radiation as infrared radiation, which is absorbed by the greenhouse gases in the atmosphere. These gases emit some of the radiation back towards the surface, raising the surface temperature.

The average surface temperature of the Earth is approximately 14°C with greenhouse gases present in the atmosphere. Without the greenhouse gases the surface temperature of the Earth would be –18°C.

The greenhouse gases in the Earth's atmosphere in order of decreasing abundance are:
- water vapour (H_2O)
- carbon dioxide (CO_2)
- methane (CH_4)
- nitrous oxide (NO)
- ozone (O_3)

Examiner tip
Noble gases cannot act as greenhouse gases because they cannot absorb infrared radiation, as they do not have any covalent bonds. Nitrogen and oxygen are the main components of air and while they contain covalent bonds, the lack of polarity of these bonds makes them virtually ineffective as greenhouse gases.

The concentration of carbon dioxide in the atmosphere has increased dramatically over the past 200 years. This is since man began to use fossil fuels prolifically. The burning of non-renewable hydrocarbon fuels releases large quantities of carbon dioxide into the atmosphere.

Carbon dioxide levels in the atmosphere were relatively consistent until 1800. This is when man started to use more and more hydrocarbon fuels to power machinery and eventually to provide electricity. The use of motor vehicles has increased the levels of carbon dioxide, particularly in the last century.

Problems caused by the greenhouse effect

There are many problems associated with increased levels of carbon dioxide in the atmosphere, but the three main ones are:
- melting of the polar ice caps, causing an increase in the sea levels
- climate change and more changeable and unpredictable weather
- global warming

Natural processes

The concentration of carbon dioxide in the atmosphere is governed by many natural processes:
- Respiration produces carbon dioxide.
- The surface waters of the Earth are a sink for carbon dioxide. Carbon dioxide dissolves in the seawater and this forms carbonates. These dissolved carbonates can precipitate out as insoluble calcium and magnesium carbonates and form part of the sediment. However, if the surface temperature of the Earth rises, the solubility of CO_2 in surface waters decreases.
- Photosynthesis uses carbon dioxide and removes it from the atmosphere.

Strategies to control, reduce and manage atmospheric carbon dioxide

Many strategies have been put in place to control, reduce and manage the concentration of carbon dioxide in the air. These include:
- raising public awareness of the problems associated with increased concentrations of carbon dioxide in the atmosphere
- city centre congestion charges to reduce vehicle emissions
- incentives to increase use of public transport
- increased road tax on less efficient vehicles
- using more renewable energy sources, which are carbon neutral, such as wind power, solar power, tidal and wave power and hydroelectric power
- worldwide treaties on carbon dioxide emissions and plans to reduce them
- increased awareness of energy efficiency in our homes, including ratings for all domestic appliances and houses overall
- 'green' awards for businesses that prove to be reducing their carbon footprint
- carbon footprint labelling for consumable items such as crisps and soft drinks

Water pollution

Nitrates are one of the main water pollutants. They come mainly from artificial fertilisers such as ammonium nitrate, NH_4NO_3. Over 60% of nitrates enter ground and surface water from agricultural land.

There are arguments for and against using artificial and natural fertilisers. These are detailed below.

Natural (organic) fertilisers

These include manure, bone meal and compost.

Knowledge check 23

Explain why carbon dioxide can act as an effective greenhouse gas.

Advantages of organic fertilisers

- As organic fertilisers break down, they improve the structure of the soil and increase its ability to hold water and nutrients.
- Since they work more slowly, they are less likely to over-fertilise the soil.
- There is little risk of build-up of toxic chemicals and salts.
- Organic fertilisers are renewable, biodegradable, sustainable and environmentally friendly.
- You can produce your own organic fertiliser, such as compost.

Disadvantages of organic fertilisers

- They act much more slowly than chemical fertilisers, because they release nutrients as they biodegrade.
- Nutrient ratios are often unknown in organic fertilisers, and the overall percentage is lower than chemical fertilisers.
- They are smelly and more difficult to apply.

Artificial (chemical) fertilisers

These include ammonium nitrate, superphosphate and triple superphosphate.

Advantages of chemical fertilisers

- They act more rapidly than organic fertilisers.
- The exact ratio of nutrients is known.
- Standardised labelling makes ratios and chemical sources easy to understand.
- They are not smelly.
- They are easier to handle as they are often in pellet or granule form, and hence easier to apply.

Disadvantages of chemical fertilisers

- Chemical fertilisers are primarily made from non-renewable sources.
- They are more expensive than organic fertilisers.
- They do not improve soil structure and can result in the depletion of trace elements in the soil.
- Because the nutrients are readily available, there is a danger of over-fertilisation.
- Chemical fertilisers tend to leach from the soil, often causing eutrophication (see below).
- Repeated applications can result in a build-up of toxic chemicals such as arsenic, cadmium and uranium in the soil.
- Long-term use of chemical fertilisers can change the soil pH and upset beneficial microbial ecosystems.

Eutrophication

Eutrophication is caused by an increase in nitrates (and phosphates) in lakes and rivers. The source of this is often leaching from artificial/chemical fertilisers from agricultural land. Eutrophication is characterised by increased algal growth. This creates competition between algae, which causes some of them to die. Decomposition of the algae by bacteria uses up oxygen in the water. The lowered levels of oxygen result in the death of fish.

Strategies to control, reduce and manage water pollution

Many strategies have been put in place to control, reduce and manage water pollution. These include:

- the use of organic fertilisers
- the use of controlled-release fertilisers
- minimum tillage of soil
- managing nitrogen fertiliser usage effectively
- using catch crops (crops grown between other crops) to prevent minerals being washed away
- denitrifying soil water using denitrifying bacteria

Waste disposal

A large proportion of household and industrial waste in the UK is plastic. Plastic waste or polymer waste is particularly worrying as it does not biodegrade and stays in the ecosystem for hundreds of years. In 2001, 7% of household waste was plastic. The methods of disposing of polymers are landfill and incineration. Both have their advantages and disadvantages.

Landfill

Disadvantages

- Landfill wastes land and often pollutes it with polymers, which will take hundreds of years to decompose.
- Some polymers can also leach compounds into the soil.
- Landfill sites are often an eyesore.
- Landfill releases methane, which is an effective greenhouse gas.

Advantages

- Landfill is the most cost-effective method of waste disposal.

Incineration

Disadvantages

- Incineration releases greenhouse gases into the air and also some toxic gases, depending on the polymer being incinerated.
- Incineration can produce gases that cause acid rain.
- Incineration still produces waste that has to be sent to landfill, but this is 90% less than it would be if it were sent directly to landfill.
- It is more expensive than landfill (but can be linked with energy recovery, where the heat of combustion is used to power an electricity generator).

Advantages

- Incineration saves money with regard to transport, as waste can be incinerated locally.
- Incineration reduces the need for unsightly landfill sites.

Strategies to control, reduce and manage waste

The European Union (EU) has guidelines about how to handle waste materials, including polymers. EU policy ranks waste management strategies in the following order:

1 Prevention of waste
2 Recycling and reuse of material
3 Safe disposal of waste that is not recyclable or re-useable — in this ranking order:
    (i) Incineration with energy recovery
    (ii) Incineration
    (iii) Landfill

Reduce, re-use, recycle

Reduce, re-use and recycle are referred to as the 3Rs. Waste management has become more and more important and we have been encouraged to reduce the amount of waste we produce. Manufacturers must limit the amount of packaging and as much packaging as possible must be able to be recycled. Reducing the amount of waste saves the Earth's resources. We are encouraged to re-use material such as carrier bags over and over again. At the end of the lifetime of an item, it should be recycled.

Strategies to reduce, control and manage polymer waste

Many strategies are already in place to reduce, control and manage polymer waste, including:

- reduction in the use of polymers in packaging
- reduction in use of carrier bags (including a set charge for them)
- dedicated polymer recycling (blue bins)
- use of biodegradable polymers
- businesses having to recycle polymers
- fines for those not recycling polymers

Summary

- Gases containing covalent bonds that absorb infrared radiation can act as greenhouse gases.
- There are advantages and disadvantages to using natural fertilisers (for example, manure) and artificial fertilisers.
- Eutrophication is caused by excessive nitrate fertiliser leaching from soil into water courses, leading to death of fish.
- Household and industrial waste can be disposed of in landfill sites or by incineration; there are advantages and disadvantages to each method of disposal, but reuse and recycling are preferred environmentally.
- Strategies are in place to reduce air, water and land pollution.

Questions & Answers

The unit test

The A2 Unit 1 examination is 2 hours in length and consists of ten multiple-choice questions (each worth 2 marks) and several structured questions, which vary in length. The structured questions make up the remaining 100 marks giving 120 marks in total for the paper. For each multiple-choice question there is one correct answer and at least one clear distractor.

About this section

Some questions in this section are followed by brief guidance on how to approach the question and also where you could make errors (shown by the icon ⊖). Answers to some questions are then followed by examiner comments. These are preceded by the icon ⊖. You could try the questions first to see how you get on and then check the answers and comments.

Lattice enthalpy, enthalpy, entropy and free energy

Question 1

> **Which one of the following is exothermic?**
> **A   enthalpy of atomisation**
> **B   first electron affinity**
> **C   first ionisation enthalpy**
> **D   lattice enthalpy**

⊖ This type of question is designed to test your knowledge of Born–Haber cycles and the associated enthalpy changes.

Answer is B

⊖ Remember that the only enthalpy changes that are exothermic in a normal cycle are generally the enthalpy change of formation and the first electron affinity. Some enthalpy changes of formation are endothermic, but this is unusual for ionic compounds as most are exothermic.

Question 2

In the blast furnace iron(III) oxide is reduced to iron by carbon monoxide according to the equation:

$$Fe_2O_3(s) + 3CO(g) \rightarrow 2Fe(s) + 3CO_2(g)$$

(a) The standard enthalpy of formation values of the reactants and products in this reaction are given in the table below. Calculate the standard enthalpy change of reaction. **(3 marks)**

Substance	ΔH_f°
$Fe_2O_3(s)$	-824
$CO(g)$	-111
$Fe(s)$	0
$CO_2(g)$	-394

(b) The standard entropy change for this reaction is $+15.2\,JK^{-1}\,mol^{-1}$. Explain why this reaction is feasible at all temperatures. **(2 marks)**

ⓔ This is a common type of synoptic question from AS2 and you need to revise this from the enthalpy section. This can be answered using a Hess's law diagram or with equations.

(a) Main equation:

$$Fe_2O_3(s) + 3CO(g) \rightarrow 2Fe(s) + 3CO_2(g)$$

Equations for given enthalpy changes:

$$2Fe(s) + 1\tfrac{1}{2}O_2(g) \rightarrow Fe_2O_3(s) \qquad -824$$
$$C(s) + \tfrac{1}{2}O_2(g) \rightarrow CO(g) \qquad -111$$
$$C(s) + O_2(g) \rightarrow CO_2(g) \qquad -394$$

_____

$$Fe_2O_3(s) \rightarrow 2Fe(s) + 1\tfrac{1}{2}\cancel{O_2(g)} \qquad +824$$

$$3CO(g) \rightarrow 3\cancel{C(s)} + 1\tfrac{1}{2}\cancel{O_2(g)} \qquad +3(111)\ ✓$$

$$3\cancel{C(s)} + 3\cancel{O_2(g)} \rightarrow 3CO_2(g) \qquad +3(-394)\ ✓$$

_____

$$Fe_2O_3(s) + 3CO(g) \rightarrow 2Fe(s) + 3CO_2(g) \qquad -25\ ✓$$

The standard enthalpy change for the reaction is $= -25\,kJ$.

ⓔ The crossed-out substances in the equations above cancel out when the overall equation is written. The sum of their enthalpy change values gives the overall value for the reaction. Remember to revise Hess's law from Energetics in AS2.

(b) The reaction is exothermic and has a positive entropy change ✓, and ΔG is negative at all temperatures ✓.

ⓔ Remember to change the standard entropy change from $JK^{-1}mol^{-1}$ to $kJK^{-1}mol^{-1}$ by dividing by 1000 as all the other units in the expression are in $kJmol^{-1}$.

Question 3

Which one of the following reactions will show a decrease in entropy?

A $CaCO_3(s) \rightarrow CaO(s) + CO_2(g)$

B $CaCO_3(s) + 2HCl(aq) \rightarrow CaCl_2(aq) + CO_2(g) + H_2O(l)$

C $NH_3(g) + HCl(g) \rightarrow NH_4Cl(s)$

D $4NH_3(g) + 5O_2(g) \rightarrow 4NO(g) + 6H_2O(g)$

Answer is C

ⓔ Enthalpy is a measure of disorder, so solids have lower enthalpy than liquids (and solutions), which have lower enthalpy than gases. Any reaction such as A and B, which produce a gas from solids and solutions, show an increase in enthalpy. A totally gaseous reaction where the number of moles of gas increases also shows an increase in entropy. An increase in the number of moles of a single state, for example moles of a substance in solution increasing, causes an increase in enthalpy.

The formation of a gas in A from a solid shows an increase in entropy and similarly in B, as gas is formed from a solid and a solution. The number of moles of gas increases in D so there is an increase in entropy. Two gases mixing to form a solid, as in C, show a decrease in enthalpy.

Kinetics

Question 1

The rate equation for the hydrolysis of 1-bromobutane is:

rate = $k[C_4H_9Br][OH^-]$

The units of the rate constant k are:

A s^{-1} C $mol^{-1}dm^3s^{-1}$

B $mol\,dm^{-3}s^{-1}$ D $mol^{-2}dm^{-6}s^{-1}$

Answer is C

ⓔ The units of *rate* are $mol\,dm^{-3}s^{-1}$ — this is the reason for answer B. There are two substances, both of which are first order of reaction. The overall order of reaction (total of the orders) is 2. Dividing $mol\,dm^{-3}s^{-1}$ by $(mol\,dm^{-3})^2$ gives $mol^{(1-2)}dm^{(-3-(-6))}s^{-1} = mol^{-1}dm^3s^{-1}$. A would be the answer where the overall order of reaction is 1 and D where the overall order of reaction is 3.

Question 2

A reacts with B to form C: A + B → C

Experiment	Initial [A] $(mol\,dm^{-3})$	Initial [B] $(mol\,dm^{-3})$	Initial rate $(\times 10^{-4}\,mol\,dm^{-3}\,s^{-1})$
1	0.1	0.1	1.99
2	0.1	0.2	7.99
3	0.2	0.1	4.00

(a) Determine the order of reaction with respect to A and B. (2 marks)

(b) Write a rate equation for the reaction. (1 mark)

(c) Using experiment 3, calculate the value of the rate constant and state its units. (2 marks)

(a) Order of reaction with respect to A = 1 ✓
Order of reaction with respect to B = 2 ✓

ⓔ As concentration of A doubles (experiment 1 to experiment 3) the rate doubles, so order of reaction with respect to A is 1. As the concentration of B doubles (experiment 1 to experiment 2) the rate quadruples (×4) so the order of reaction with respect to B is 2.

(b) rate = $k[A][B]^2$ ✓
(c) $4.00 \times 10^{-4} = k(0.2)(0.1)^2$

$$k = \frac{4.0 \times 10^{-4}}{2 \times 10^3} = 0.2 \checkmark\ mol^{-2}dm^6s^{-1} \checkmark$$

Equilibrium and acid–base equilibria

Question 1

Which of the following equilibrium constants will always have units?
  A K_w **C** K_d
  B K_c **D** K_p

Answer is A

ⓔ K_d never has units because it is concentration of a solute in one layer divided by concentration of the same solute in a different layer. K_c and K_p may have units depending on the concentrations and partial pressures on the top and bottom lines in the expression. K_w always has units ($mol^2\,dm^{-6}$). Any p value such as pH, pK_a or pOH does not have units.

Question 2

Ethanol reacts with ethanoic acid according to the equation:

$$CH_3CH_2OH + CH_3COOH \rightleftharpoons CH_3COOCH_2CH_3 + H_2O$$

K_c for this reaction is 4.1 at 30°C.

(a) Write an equilibrium expression for this reaction. (1 mark)

(b) Explain why K_c for this reaction has no units. (1 mark)

(c) Calculate the number of moles of ethyl ethanoate formed when 1 mol of ethanol reacts
with 1 mol of ethanoic acid at 30°C. (2 marks)

(a) $K_c = \dfrac{[CH_3COOCH_2CH_3][H_2O]}{[CH_3CH_2OH][CH_3COOH]}$ ✓

ⓔ The equilibrium expression is based on the balanced symbol equation for the reaction where
the powers in the equilibrium expression are the balancing numbers in the equation.

(b) Concentrations on top of the expression cancel out concentrations on the
bottom. ✓

ⓔ If the powers cancel out top and bottom in the expression then there are no units of K_c.

(c)

$K_c = \dfrac{x^2}{(1-x)^2}$

$\left(\dfrac{x}{1-x}\right)^2 = 4.1$

$\left(\dfrac{x}{1-x}\right) = 2.02$ ✓

$x = 2.02(1-x)$

$x = 2.02 - 2.02x$

$3.02x = 2.02$

$x = \dfrac{2.02}{3.02} = 0.67$ ✓

ⓔ If the moles of ethanoic acid or ethanol were asked for, the answer would be $1 - x$. This is
very common in equilibrium questions. Be careful you check exactly what value you are asked for
as it could be x or some other value involving x.

Question 3

Complete the table calculating the pH of the resulting solutions in the following examples.

	Solution		pH
(a)	25.0 cm³ of 0.1 M hydrochloric acid	(1 mark)	
(b)	20.0 cm³ of 0.1 M sodium hydroxide solution added to 30.0 cm³ of 0.1 M ethanoic acid ($K_a = 1.8 \times 10^{-5}$ mol dm⁻³)	(4 marks)	

ⓔ For part (b) it is important to realise before you start that this is a buffer and not a straightforward neutralisation. You need to determine the concentration of the weak acid and its salt after reaction.

(a) pH = –log(0.1) = 1

ⓔ The volume is not important when the concentration of the acid is stated. The concentration of the hydrochloric acid is 0.1 M, so [H⁺] = 0.1 M as it is a monobasic acid. Hence pH = –log(0.1) = 1.

(b)

$$\text{moles of ethanoic} = \frac{(30.0 \times 0.1)}{1000} = 0.003$$

$$\text{moles of NaOH} = \frac{(20.0 \times 0.1)}{1000} = 0.002$$

$$CH_3COOH + NaOH \rightarrow CH_3COONa + H_2O$$

moles of ethanoic acid remaining = 0.003 – 0.002 = 0.001

moles of sodium ethanoate formed = 0.002

total volume of solution = 50.0 cm³

$$\text{new concentration of ethanoic acid} = \frac{0.001}{50} \times 1000 = 0.02\,M \checkmark$$

$$\text{new concentration of ethanoate ions} = \frac{0.002}{50} \times 1000 = 0.04\,M \checkmark$$

$$K_a = \frac{[H^+]\,[CH_3COO^-]}{[CH_3COOH]} = \frac{([H^+] \times 0.04)}{0.02} = 1.8 \times 10^{-5}$$

$$[H^+] = \frac{(1.8 \times 10^{-5} \times 0.02)}{0.04} = 9.0 \times 10^{-6}\,M \checkmark$$

pH = –log[H⁺] = –log(9.0 × 10⁻⁶) = 5.05 ✓

Isomerism, aldehydes, ketones, carboxylic acids, esters and fats

Question 1

Which one of the following compounds will react with Tollens' reagent?
  A $CH_3COCH_2CH_3$ C CH_3CH_2CHO
  B $CH_3COOCH_2CH_3$ D CH_3CH_2COOH

Answer is C

ⓔ Aldehydes react with Tollens' reagent, Fehling's solution and acidified potassium dichromate solution. Aldehydes undergo mild oxidation. Remember from AS2 that primary and secondary alcohols also undergo mild oxidation and will react with acidified potassium dichromate solution. C is an aldehyde; you can recognise it from the CHO functional group. A is a ketone (CO group), B is an ester (COO group) and D is a carboxylic acid (COOH group).

Question 2

The following organic reaction scheme shows a series of reactions:

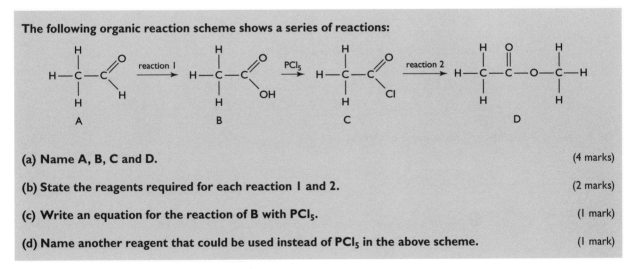

(a) Name A, B, C and D.   (4 marks)

(b) State the reagents required for each reaction 1 and 2.   (2 marks)

(c) Write an equation for the reaction of B with PCl₅.   (1 mark)

(d) Name another reagent that could be used instead of PCl₅ in the above scheme. (1 mark)

ⓔ This is a common type of question involving organic compounds from different sections of the specification. It is important to note that A2 units may have synoptic questions from AS. Make sure you revise intermolecular forces, shapes of molecules and redox from AS1. Also look at the organic chemistry from AS2 as well as enthalpy, equilibrium and kinetics.

(a) A is ethanal ✓   C is ethanoyl chloride ✓
       B is ethanoic acid ✓   D is methyl ethanoate ✓

ⓔ Look for the functional groups. Organic reactions focus on the change from one functional group to another. A has a CHO functional group and is an aldehyde; B has a COOH functional group and is a carboxylic acid; C has a COCl functional group and is an acid chloride; D is an ester as it has the COO functional group. Organic reactions change one functional group into another functional group.

(b) Reaction 1 — any mild oxidising agent, for example acidified potassium dichromate solution. ✓
Tollens' reagent and Fehling's solution are used as tests for aldehydes and ketones but acidified potassium dichromate would be the preferred reagent for the mild oxidation of aldehydes.
Reaction 2 — methanol/CH_3OH ✓

(c) $CH_3COOH + PCl_5 \rightarrow CH_3COCl + POCl_3 + HCl$ ✓

(d) thionyl chloride/$SOCl_2$ ✓

Question 3

The following pure fat is a solid at room temperature:

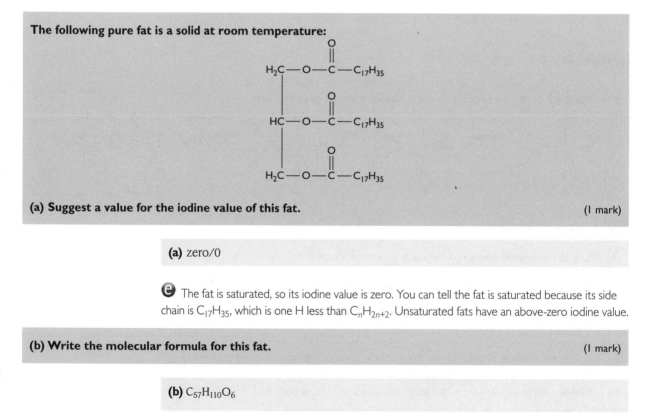

(a) Suggest a value for the iodine value of this fat.   (1 mark)

(a) zero/0

ⓔ The fat is saturated, so its iodine value is zero. You can tell the fat is saturated because its side chain is $C_{17}H_{35}$, which is one H less than C_nH_{2n+2}. Unsaturated fats have an above-zero iodine value.

(b) Write the molecular formula for this fat.   (1 mark)

(b) $C_{57}H_{110}O_6$

ⓔ The total numbers for carbon, hydrogen and oxygen atoms in the molecule are added up. A molecular formula shows the total number of each type of atom present in a compound.

Question 4

0.8 g of an oil was refluxed with 25.0 cm³ of 1 M potassium hydroxide solution for 1 hour. The resulting solution was titrated against 0.1 M hydrochloric acid. The titre was 14.8 cm³. The process was repeated with no oil and the titre was found to be 26.2 cm³. Calculate the saponification value of the oil.

moles of HCl = moles of KOH in 25.0 cm³ (without oil) = 0.00262

moles of HCl = moles of KOH in 25.0 cm³ (with oil) = 0.00148

moles of KOH that reacted with oil = 0.00262 – 0.00148 = 0.00114

mass of KOH that reacted with the oil = 0.00114 × 56 = 0.06384 g = 63.84 mg

mass (mg) of KOH which reacted with 1 g of the oil = $\frac{63.84}{0.8}$ = 79.8

Question 5

Which one of the following molecules exhibits optical isomerism?
A $CH_2(OH)CH_2COOH$ C $CH_3CH_2CH_2CHO$
B $CH_3CH(OH)CH_3$ D $CH_3CH(OH)COOH$

Answer is D

ⓔ The molecule with a chiral centre (four different groups bonded to the same carbon atom) exhibits optical isomerism. Quickly draw the structures of the organic molecules in this type of question to determine the molecule with a chiral centre.

Periodic trends and environmental chemistry

Question 1

Which of the following substances is not a greenhouse gas?
A   carbon dioxide   C   neon
B   methane   D   water vapour

Answer is C

ⓔ All the other substances have covalent bonds, which would absorb infrared radiation and then emit it back to the surface of the Earth, making them greenhouse gases. Neon does not form compounds and so does not have covalent bonds. Infrared radiation (AS 2) is absorbed by molecules containing covalent bonds, which can undergo molecular vibrations (bending and stretching).

Question 2

The chlorides of period 3 elements dissolve or react with water.

(a) State the pH of a solution of sodium chloride. (1 mark)

(b) Write an equation for the reaction of PCl_5 with water. (1 mark)

(c) Describe the bonding in a sample of solid aluminium chloride. (2 marks)

(a) 7 ✓

ⓔ The pH of a solution of a salt of a strong base and a strong acid is 7 (neutral).

(b)

$$PCl_5 + H_2O \rightarrow POCl_3 + 2HCl$$

or

$$PCl_5 + 4H_2O \rightarrow H_3PO_4 + 5HCl \checkmark$$

ⓔ The first equation can be worked out from the reaction of PCl_5 with water containing an OH group. $POCl_3$ is phosphorus oxychloride (phosphorus(v) trichloride oxide).

(c) covalent ✓ and coordinate ✓

ⓔ Al_2Cl_6 exists as a dimer with covalent and coordinate bonds. Make sure you can draw the dot-and-cross diagram for Al_2Cl_6, showing the coordinate bonds and the covalent bonds.

Question 3

Which of the following oxides of period 3 elements produces the most alkaline solution on reaction with water?

A	Na_2O	C	SO_2
B	MgO	D	Cl_2O_7

Answer is A

ⓔ The metal oxides are basic or amphoteric. Basic oxides react with acids but some may react with water to form alkaline solutions. Sodium oxide reacts with water to form sodium hydroxide solution. Magnesium oxide has low solubility in water because it has a strong ionic lattice. The oxides of non-metal oxides are acidic (some other non-metal oxides are neutral, such as H_2O and CO).

Knowledge check answers

1 The standard enthalpy change of atomisation is the enthalpy change when 1 mol of gaseous atoms is formed from the element in its standard state.
2 Standard change in entropy
3 $kJ\,mol^{-1}$
4 The rate constant is the proportionality constant that links the rate of reaction to the concentrations in the rate equation.
5 Nucleophilic substitution/S_N1
6 $K_c = \dfrac{[NO_2]^2}{[N_2O_4]}$ units are $mol\,dm^{-3}$
7 1
8 It moves the position of equilibrium to the right. There is no effect on K_p.
9 OH^-/hydroxide ions
10 $pH = -log[H^+]$
11 $pH = -log(0.4) = 0.398$
12 $K_a = \dfrac{[CH_3COO^-][H^+]}{[CH_3COOH]}$
13 A solution that resists small changes in pH when small volumes of acid and alkali are added.
14 Pink
15 Unable to rotate the plane of plane-polarised light.
16 Nucleophilic addition
17 $CH_3CH_2CH_2COOH + 4[H] \rightarrow CH_3CH_2CH_2CH_2OH + H_2O$
18 Methyl propanoate
19 Mass of potassium hydroxide in mg that is required to completely hydrolyse 1 g of a fat or oil.
20 A higher iodine value means less saturated or a lower iodine value means more saturated.
21 Sodium oxide
22 Sodium chloride
23 It has covalent bonds, which bend and stretch as they absorb infrared radiation.

Index

Note: **bold** page numbers indicate definitions of key terms.